METHUEN'S
MONOGRAPHS ON
PHYSICAL SUBJECTS

General Editor
B. L. WORSNOP, B.Sc., Ph.D.

IONIZATION AND
BREAKDOWN IN GASES

Ionization and Breakdown in Gases

F. LLEWELLYN-JONES

M.A. (OXON), D.PHIL., D.SC. (OXON), F.INST.P.

Professor of Physics, University of Wales;
Head of Department of Physics,
University College of Swansea

LONDON: METHUEN & CO LTD
NEW YORK: JOHN WILEY & SONS INC

First published in 1957

CATALOGUE NO. 4066/U

PRINTED IN GREAT BRITAIN
BY RICHARD CLAY & COMPANY LTD
BUNGAY, SUFFOLK

TO MY WIFE

Contents

7

Preface

The aim of this monograph is to give a brief account of the fundamental physics of the electrical breakdown of gases, and the book is primarily intended for the postgraduate research worker and honours-degree student. In taking into account work carried out in recent years, an attempt is made to assess how much of the subject is now amenable to systematic treatment, and to indicate where there is still need of more quantitative experimental data. It is hoped that the book will help towards an understanding of the fundamental principles of the motions of electrons and ions in gases, and towards providing a physical picture of the processes which bring about the fascinating phenomenon of the electric spark—a phenomenon which has attracted scientific interest for more than a century. The presentation adopted here is based on a course of lectures to postgraduate research students and to undergraduates in the honours school of physics at Swansea.

The macroscopic phenomena of drift, current growth, emission of light, and chemical changes, etc., may be quantitatively related to the atomic processes by the dynamical theory of gases, the theory being applied to charged and uncharged particles alike. In this monograph a knowledge of elementary classical statistical mechanics is assumed on the part of the reader. For a quantitative discussion of electronic, atomic, and ionic collision processes which can be accomplished only by wave mechanics, the reader is referred to well-known textbooks. Treatment of maintained electrical discharges, such as the glow or arc, is excluded, and attention is confined to an account of recent researches, theoretical as well as experimental, on the electrical breakdown of a gas, especially in so far as the mechanism which sets the criterion for the breakdown is concerned. Comprehensive accounts of experimental data or detailed descriptions of the techniques of measuring ionization currents, their temporal growth, impulse voltage production, and oscillographic recording are not given, for such information is best obtained from the original papers.

Full references will be found in the textbooks and reviews listed in the Bibliography.

I am particularly indebted to my colleagues, Dr P. M. Davidson for much valuable discussion and Drs J. Dutton and C. G. Morgan, for reading and criticizing much of the manuscript and checking the proofs. My thanks are also due to Professor F. M. Bruce and the publishers of *Endeavour* for permission to reproduce the photographs in Plates I and II; to the Royal Society for Figs. 5.1, 5.3, 5.4, 5.5, 5.7, 5.8, 5.9, 6.4, 6.5, and 6.6; to the Physical Society for Figs. 4.6, 4.7, 4.8, 7.2, 7.3, 7.4, 7.6, and 9.1 to 9.6 inclusive; to the Institute of Physics for Figs. 8.4 and 8.5; to the American Institute of Electrical Engineers for Figs. 6.1 and 6.2; to the Institute of Physics, New York for Fig. 8.6; to the publishers of *Nature* for Fig. 5.2; and to Messrs. Methuen and Co. Ltd. for Figs. 2.4 and 2.5.

F. LLEWELLYN-JONES

Swansea, 1956

CHAPTER I

Introduction

1.1 Technological and Scientific Aspects of Electrical Breakdown in Gases

A gas in its normal state is almost a perfect insulator, and in everyday life is widely used in that role. However, when an electric force of sufficient intensity is established in the gas between two electrodes, the gas can become a conductor, and the transition from an insulating to an almost completely conducting state is called the electrical breakdown.

Modern technological developments have accentuated interest in the electrical breakdown of gases. Electrical power-transmission systems are in operation at some 400,000 V., and even higher voltages are now contemplated. Such high voltages create problems of cable insulation and of circuit breaking. Where the transmission is effected by overhead lines, the insulation is provided by the air surrounding the conductors. When it is necessary to use underground cable instead of overhead lines, the cable is contained in a sealed tube and insulated by gas at a pressure considerably greater than atmospheric. High-pressure gas insulation is also being used in an attempt to render high-voltage machines (such as X-ray generators for deep-ray therapy) conveniently small for general application in hospitals.

In general, the many useful applications of the spark discharge are due to two main properties: the extreme rapidity of the transition it produces from almost perfect insulation to almost perfect conduction in a gas, and the ability of the discharge gap itself to pass high currents and then recover its original insulating state. The breakdown of a gap thus serves the purpose of a very good switch, and indeed, as such, finds very wide application in timing apparatus or in switches which have to operate at rates quite impossible with mechanical devices. In modern electronics breakdown is utilized in apparatus such as flash tubes, Geiger counters, and thyratrons.

In many applications the electric field which produces breakdown is static, or only slowly varying (e.g., power frequency), and is established in the gas by means of two metal electrodes connected to a source of high potential. In such cases, as might be expected, the nature of the metals themselves can play an important part in determining the particular ionization processes which contribute to the electrical breakdown. Breakdown can also be produced by alternating electric fields, and this is especially the case for fields alternating at high frequency when the gas pressure is low; internal electrodes are then not necessary, as the required field can be applied by induction from a remote conductor. Discharges produced in this way are in recent years finding considerable application as ion sources in nuclear physics; the low energy of the positive ions which can be drawn out from the glowing gas provide a nearly monoenergetic beam. High-frequency fields are also being used for light sources in spectroscopy.

The importance of the scientific investigation of the mechanism of the breakdown process is mainly due to the fact that control both of the initiation and of the suppression of a spark may be better achieved from an understanding of the physics of the spark.

The gas-collisional and electrode surface phenomena such as occur in the electrical breakdown of gases are of fundamental interest to the physicist, and much information can be gained from a study of breakdown phenomena.

1.2 Breakdown Phenomena

The range of breakdown phenomena is very wide, embracing the lightning flash or the gigantic spark from high-voltage equipment on the one hand, and the low-voltage microscopic spark found at the operation of an electrical contact on the other, and over this range the various phenomena appear so different that, to account for them, different views have from time to time been put forward.

The strong interest of the subject of electrical breakdown of gases both to the practical electrical engineer and to the physicist has had, however, the unfortunate effect during the last quarter of a century of producing some confusion in the elucidation and treatment of the subject of breakdown.

The electrical engineer is often concerned that a given gas should maintain its insulating properties in the presence of high electric fields, and he regards breakdown as the acquisition of completely conducting properties by the gas, to produce, say, a complete short-circuit. Thus, to the electrical engineer, breakdown often means the complete build-up of a current in a previously insulating space—but insulating only as far as high currents are concerned. The physicist, on the other hand, has, perhaps, tended to be concerned with other aspects of the process. Before a large current can develop in a previously insulating gas, it is clear that the current must build up by some ionization mechanism from an extremely small value or even only a few initiatory electrons. Such small ionization currents themselves hardly affect the operation of high-power equipment, so that the engineer feels less concerned with these. However, when the electrical conditions, or criteria, for the occurrence of breakdown are satisfied, then such small electron currents can themselves build up to the high currents which constitute final flash-over. The physicist has therefore tended to regard electrical breakdown from the point of view of investigating the physical conditions which permit the ionization processes to produce the amplification of the current, the elucidation of the general mechanism by which this can occur, and finally, the identification of the fundamental ionization processes themselves.

The physical cause of breakdown lies in the electrical conditions which permit a small electron current to build up to a value which is practically limited only by the external circuit. It is all the more surprising that until very recently so little attention has been given to the important aspect of the spatio-temporal growth of an ionization current from its extremely small beginnings to the high values finally attainable when the criterion for electrical breakdown is satisfied. This neglect, in fact, has been the cause of considerable misunderstanding concerning the true nature of the breakdown criterion. The problem of breakdown is less one of investigating the fundamental collision processes themselves than of identifying the particular processes predominating in any given case, and of finding the general mechanism by which those processes interact to produce the observed growth of current.

1.3 Scheme of Present Treatment of the Subject

The problem of complete gaseous breakdown can well be considered in two aspects: first, the elucidation of the mechanism which sets the criterion which must be satisfied before breakdown is at all possible; and secondly, the mechanism by which an ionization current can increase, when once the breakdown criterion is satisfied, to produce first a glow discharge and then the glow-to-arc transition. The following chapters, although mainly concerned with the first aspect of the breakdown problem, namely, the elucidation of the mechanism which sets the criterion for breakdown in static fields, will also consider the important problem of the initial stage of the growth of ionization after the criterion for breakdown has been satisfied. These are the stages which, so far, have yielded to quantitative treatment.

Before considering the mechanism of current amplification in the gas, it is first necessary to discuss fundamental principles of the motions of electrons and ions in gases, and the statistical equilibrium of such assemblies. This is done in Chapter II; Chapter III gives a brief outline of the ionization processes which occur in the gas or at surfaces, and which might be of importance in breakdown.

The breakdown mechanism itself is then discussed in the succeeding chapters. The procedure is first to consider the case which might be regarded as the simplest from the physical point of view, namely, that of the static uniform electric field at the lower gas pressures. This is done in Chapter IV. The following chapters then consider progressive complications which might be introduced by changes of the various parameters such as gas pressure, electrode surface activity, gap distance, still all for the uniform static field. These aspects are considered in Chapters V and VI. Chapter VII considers the further complication due to non-uniformity of the field brought about by gap geometry, but still for static fields.

The complicated question of the non-steady state, i.e., the development of ionization in time, when a sufficiently high voltage is applied to a gap is considered in Chapter VIII. In recent years considerable work has been done on this important aspect, and this chapter attempts to assess the present position, put forward the new flash-growth concept of breakdown development, and also to indicate where there is most need for further experimental data.

The book concludes with a brief outline of breakdown under high-frequency fields.

CHAPTER II

Dynamical Theory of the Motion of Charged Particles in an Ideal Gas [1]

2.1 Simple Collisions

An *elastic* collision is one in which there are no internal changes of energy in the colliding particles; only redistribution of the kinetic energy of the colliding particles is involved. An *inelastic* collision involves, in addition, internal changes of energy undergone by the atom or molecule, so that the total kinetic energy of the particles is different after the collision from what it was before. There are different kinds of inelastic collisions.

This chapter is concerned with the elementary principles of transport phenomena; diffusion of the ions and electrons away from the space concerned; drift of the particles down the electric field; the attainment of mean energies greater than the thermal value; and the distribution of the energies of the particles about the mean, the treatment being based on the dynamical theory of an ideal gas.

2.2 Free Paths

The theory of an ideal gas (see, for example, Jeans, *Dynamical Theory of Gases*, Chapter X) leads to the following expression for the mean free path L_1 of the particles of one ideal gas of small concentration n_1 and mean energy of agitation $E_1 = \frac{1}{2}mu^2$ in another ideal gas of concentration n_2 and mean energy $E_2 = \frac{1}{2}MU^2$ and σ_{12} is the distance between centres of the spherical particles when in contact.

$$L_1 = 1/n_2\pi\sigma_{12}{}^2(1 + U^2/u^2)^{\frac{1}{2}} \quad . \quad . \quad . \quad (2.1)$$

When equipartition of energy is established between the various types of particles, the mean energy of each type is represented by

$$\tfrac{1}{2}mu^2 = \tfrac{1}{2}MU^2 = 3kT/2 \quad . \quad . \quad . \quad . \quad (2.2)$$

[1] The undergraduate student may well at first defer detailed reading of this chapter, which is mainly mathematical, and proceed to Chapter III.

where k is Boltzmann's constant. The mean energy of agitation being then proportional to the absolute temperature T. Thus in an assembly of electrons and atoms in thermal equilibrium the mean electron energy can be referred to as a temperature, which is then the same as that of the gas atoms because the temperature is defined dynamically by relation (2.2).

The mean free path L_a of atoms in their own gas is given by

$$L_a = 1/\sqrt{2}n_2\pi\sigma_{12}{}^2 \quad . \quad . \quad . \quad . \quad (2.3)$$

since in 2.1, $E_1 = E_2$, and $m = M$, and $\sigma_{12}/2$ = the atomic radius σ. If it is assumed that an ion is merely an ideal atom which is charged, and the kinetic theory is applied, then the mean free path of the ion $L_+ = L_a$. Charged particles, however, can polarize neutral molecules producing mutual attraction and so shorten the free path. J. J. Thomson [259] examined this effect and obtained an expression:

$$L_+ = L_a(\Omega/RT)^{-\frac{1}{2}}$$

where T is the absolute temperature, Ω is the potential energy of an ion when in contact with an atom, and R the gas constant. On this view the normal mean free path of a slow ion can be considerably reduced in a highly polarizable gas.

In the case of electrons colliding with gas atoms, even if in thermal equilibrium, $u^2 >> U^2$, since m/M is small (e.g., electrons in thermal equilibrium with mercury vapour have a mean speed 10^3 times greater than that of the Hg atoms), so that their mean free path l_m is given by

$$l_m = 1/n_2\pi\sigma^2 = 4\sqrt{2}L_a = 4\sqrt{2}L_+ \quad . \quad . \quad (2.4)$$

2.3 Fractional Energy Loss and Scattering

Consider two spherical particles of masses m and M about to collide: for our purposes it is sufficient to consider one of the particles to be at rest and the other to have a velocity u_0 before collision. After collision particle m rebounds with velocity u_1 and M moves along the line of centres.

The fractional loss of energy of m in collision at angle θ is

$$\Delta(\theta) = (u_0{}^2 - u_1{}^2)/u_0{}^2$$

Momentum and energy equations are

$$\left.\begin{array}{c} mu_0 - mu_1\cos\psi = MV\cos\theta \\ mu_1\sin\psi = MV\sin\theta \end{array}\right\} \quad . \quad (2.5)$$

$$mu_0{}^2 - mu_1{}^2 = MV^2 \quad . \quad . \quad . \quad . \quad (2.6)$$

Thus $\qquad\qquad\qquad \Delta(\theta) = MV^2/mu_0^2$ . . (2.7)

Squaring and adding equation 2.5 and using 2.6

$$V = 2mu_0 \cos \theta/(M + m) \qquad \text{. . .} \qquad (2.8)$$

Let $P(\theta)$ be the probability of a collision at an angle θ. The total area presented for collision is $\pi\sigma_{12}^2$. Thus the probability of a collision

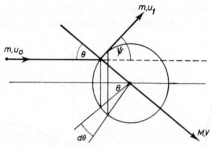

FIG. 2.1. Collision of elastic spheres of masses m and M

taking place between θ and $\theta + d\theta$ is the ratio of the projected area $2\pi\sigma_{12}^2 \sin \theta \cos \theta d\theta$ to the whole area $\pi\sigma_{12}^2$, i.e.,

$$P(\theta)d\theta = 2\pi\sigma_{12}^2 \sin \theta \cos \theta d\theta/\pi\sigma_{12}^2 = \sin 2\theta d\theta \quad . \quad (2.9)$$

Thus the mean fractional loss of energy allowing for collisions at all possible angles is

$$\Delta = \overline{\Delta(\theta)} = \int_0^{\pi/2} P(\theta)\Delta(\theta)d\theta \Big/ \int_0^{\pi/2} P(\theta)d\theta \quad . \quad (2.10)$$

and using equations 2.6, 2.8, and 2.9, this is

$$= 2mM/(m + M)^2 \qquad \text{. . . .} \qquad (2.11)$$

Ions. Putting $m = M$, equation 2.11 gives $\Delta = \frac{1}{2}$. This result is sufficient to indicate the high rate of loss of energy experienced by, say, positive ions when moving through a gas of much lower mean energy. The case when the ion and atom velocities have a Maxwellian distribution has been treated by Cravath [47].

Also expression 2.9 gives the probability $P(\psi)$ of the ion being scattered at angle ψ, and equations 2.5 to 2.9 gives $\psi = \pi/2 - \theta$, and

$$P(\psi)d\psi = \sin 2\psi d\psi \qquad \text{. . . .} \qquad (2.12)$$

This function is illustrated in Fig. 2.2.

The fractional numbers of particles scattered per unit solid angle is

$$I(\psi) = P(\psi)d\psi/d\omega = \sin 2\psi \, d\psi/2\pi \sin \psi d\psi \quad . \quad (2.13)$$

$$= \cos \psi/\pi$$

Electrons. Putting $m \ll M$, equations 2.5 to 2.11 give

$$\Delta = 2m/M \quad . \quad . \quad . \quad . \quad (2.14)$$

This can be regarded as applying to a group of electrons of mean energy large compared with that of the gas atoms. For the case of

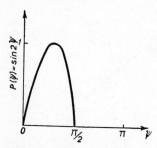

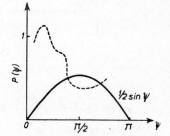

Fig. 2.2. Elastic scattering of ions (neglecting charges): only forward scattering occurs, i.e., there is persistence of motion

Fig. 2.3. Elastic scattering of electrons. Full-line curve corresponds to ideal elastic spheres for which back scattering is as probable as forward scattering. Dotted curve corresponds to observations with 10 eV electrons in mercury vapour [173]

electrons moving through helium, $\Delta = 2.73 \times 10^{-4}$, and such a value was found by Townsend and Bailey [263] from their experiments on the lateral diffusion of electrons in gases, and by Franck and Hertz in their energy-loss experiments; Δ is, of course, lower for heavier atoms.

This low value of Δ for electrons is the reason why a cloud of electrons can acquire high mean energies under comparatively low electric fields and thermal equilibrium between electrons and gas atoms is upset. Similarly, because of the high value of Δ for ions, the mean energies of ions in an ideal gas are low at low fields, and thermal equilibrium with the gas atoms is hardly disturbed. When an electric field is removed ions very quickly attain thermal equilibrium with gas atoms; electrons take longer.

To consider the elastic scattering of electrons, put $m/M << 1$ in equations 2.5 to 2.8 from which $\psi = \pi - 2\theta$, and

$$\Delta(\theta) = 2m(1 - \cos \psi)/M \quad . \quad . \quad . \quad (2.15)$$

and

$$P(\psi)d\psi = \sin \psi d\psi/2 \quad . \quad . \quad . \quad (2.16)$$

This scattering function is illustrated in Fig. 2.3. The distribution of scattered electrons per unit solid angle $I(\psi)$, is

$$P(\psi)d\psi/d\omega = \sin \psi d\psi/4\pi \sin \psi d\psi = 1/4\pi \quad . \quad (2.17)$$

The scattering is thus spherically symmetrical, i.e., uniform, and all directions of motion after collision are equally probable. $I(\psi)$ is the function usually measured: the angle scattering function $P(\psi)$ is obtained by multiplying the observed $I(\psi)$ by $2\pi \sin \psi$.

2.4 Effective Cross-section

2.4.1 *Elastic Collisions.* The particular ideal scattering distribution given in equation 2.17 is not generally found in practice. The work of Bullard and Massey, and of Arnot, showed that the scattering of low-energy electrons by, say, mercury atoms, is indicated more by the dotted line in Fig. 2.3. Such results are explicable in terms of the wave mechanics of the electron, and may be taken approximately to indicate diffraction of the electron wave by the atom field [10, 173]. The difference between the quantum and classical theories of scattering becomes acute for small angles of scattering. Indeed, on the classical view regarding an atom as a centre of coulomb force, the atomic cross-section for elastic scattering should be infinite, because some deviation, however small, must be suffered by every electron passing through such a field: determinations of elastic cross-section would then depend upon the resolving power of the apparatus. This difficulty is resolved by wave mechanics; Mott has pointed out that by applying the uncertainty principle for small angles of scattering, a finite cross-section can be specified. One consequence is the fact that the cross-section q depends on the velocity u of the electrons, as well as on the scattering angle ψ.

Consider electrons being scattered, with small change of energy, by atoms (N per unit volume), a law of scattering may be specified as follows. If per unit volume there are dn electrons all moving in the same direction with velocity u and total momentum dM, a number $N\pi\sigma^2(u)udn$ is scattered per unit time. Of this number the fraction scattered in directions making angles between ψ and $\psi + d\psi$ with the direction of the original beam is $f(\psi, u)d\psi$. Thus

$$\int_0^\pi f(\psi, u)d\psi = 1 . \quad . \quad . \quad . \quad . \quad (2.18)$$

The momentum along the direction of u lost per electron at each ψ scattering is nearly $dM(1 - \cos \psi)/dn$, and the total loss of momentum by the dn electrons is evidently

$$N\pi\sigma^2(u)g(u)dM,$$

where

$$g(u) = \int_0^\pi (1 - \cos \psi)f(\psi, u)d\psi \quad . \quad . \quad . \quad (2.19)$$

The fraction of the dn electrons making collisions in unit time is $u/l(u)$ where $l(u)$ is the mean free path of the electron for collision. Thus, from 2.4

$$l(u) = 1/N\pi\sigma^2(u) \quad . \quad . \quad . \quad . \quad . \quad (2.20)$$

Similarly, if the fractional loss of momentum per unit time by the u electrons is written $u/l_m(u)$, then $l_m(u)$ is called the mean free path for momentum transfer. Evidently

$$l_m(u) = 1/N\pi\sigma^2(u)g(u) \quad . \quad . \quad . \quad . \quad (2.21)$$

and the cross-section for momentum transfer is thus

$$Q_m(u) = Q_e(u)\overline{(1 - \cos \psi)} = Q_e(u)g(u) \quad . \quad (2.22)$$

where Q_e is the cross-section for scattering.

For elastic spheres, $f(\psi, u) = f(\psi) = (\sin \psi)/2$ and the average value of ψ is $\pi/2$, giving $\cos \psi = 0$; but if there is any pronounced forward scattering $\overline{\cos \psi}$ is positive, while if mainly backward $\overline{\cos \psi}$ is negative. Thus expressions derived on the basis of classical elastic scattering may be suitably modified by using 2.22 to take into account asymmetrical scattering.

Townsend and Bailey [281] in 1920–23 measured the mean free path of electrons in gases at low pressures for various values of the ratio field over gas pressure (i.e., mean electron energy, see § 2.7). These experiments enabled the cross-section to be plotted as a function of mean electron energy over an important range of low energies (1–5 eV), and a marked variation of cross-section with electron energy was found, being especially great for the monatomic gases helium and argon. About the same time, Ramsauer and co-workers

[217] investigated the scattering of a monoenergetic beam of electrons at extremely low pressures over a range of high energy (20–100 eV). Later Ramsauer extended his measurements to the lower range and found results similar to those of Townsend and Bailey. Typical results are illustrated in Fig. 2.4. This phenomenon, known as the Townsend–Ramsauer effect, has an important bearing on the values of those quantities which depend on atomic cross-sections, e.g., electron-energy distribution function, and therefore of the coefficients of mobilities, diffusion, ionization, and excitation.

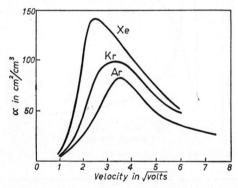

Fig. 2.4. Total effective cross-section curves for xenon, krypton, and argon [10]

2.4.2 *Inelastic Collisions.* If Q_0 is an elastic cross-section the rate of elastic collisions is then uQ_0. However, even if an electron has sufficient energy it does not follow that excitation to a level V_i occurs at every collision; the rate is then defined using a probability factor $P_i(E_1)$ such that the rate of excitation to the given level depends on $Q_0 P_i(E_1)$. This quantity is often referred to as the cross-section Q_i for the particular excitation. These probability functions have been determined experimentally for the various excitation levels by Hanle [106], Michels [182], Lees [139], and by others [173] and for ionization by Compton and van Voorhis [43], and Smith and his collaborators [17]. Typical classes are illustrated in Fig. 2.5.

The shape of these curves can be explained by considering the conservation of linear momentum of the colliding particles, and the quantum selection rules relating to electron spin.

These various cross-sections for elastic scattering, excitation, and ionization lead to the conception of the total effective cross-section Q defined by

$$Q = Q_0 + \Sigma Q_n$$

where Q_n represents the cross-section for an inelastic collision exciting to the nth level.

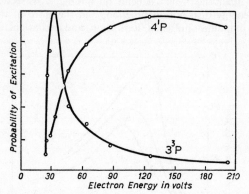

(a) Excitation function for the 4^1P and 3^3P levels of helium

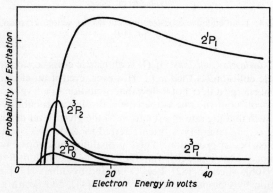

(b) Theoretical excitation functions for four P levels of mercury

FIG. 2.5. Probability function P_i for excitation to triplet levels has a sharp maximum near the excitation potential, while for singlet levels P_i has a gradual rise to a maximum. Ionization resembles the case for singlet levels [10]

2.5 Transport

When the electric field is very low the electrons and gas molecules are nearly in statistical equilibrium, and the electron-energy distribution is nearly Maxwellian. For higher fields the mean electron energy is increased, and the distribution changes to one determined by the energy losses in collision. The transport of electrons or ions under these conditions have been investigated by Townsend [275, 277, 278], Huxley and Zaazou [122], Druyvesteyn [62, 63, 64], Didlaukis [59], Morse, Larmar and Allis [190], Davydov [57], Allis and Allen [8], Davidson [54]. The following discussion is based on a treatment due to Davidson using the velocity diagram.

Suppose that the electrons are in a uniform field, acting on each electron of charge e with a force eE in the x direction, thus giving it an acceleration $eE/m = C$, say, and therefore, in the velocity diagram, a velocity C in the x direction. Let the electrons in a unit volume of space have, when represented in a velocity diagram, a density $\rho(x, u, \theta)$, where θ is the inclination to the x axis. The function ρ may be written as

$$\rho = \rho_0(x, u) + \rho_1(x, u, \theta)$$

where ρ_1 has a value zero when averaged over a spherical shell in the velocity diagram. The current is, of course, due entirely to ρ_1. Usually ρ_1 and its variations in the velocity diagram are small compared with ρ_0 and its variations; in the calculations this will be assumed.

Consider a shell (in the velocity diagram) of radius u and thickness du; the electrons in it contribute to the total current density (of particles) an amount, say, $i_u du$, which, when multiplied by the electronic mass m, is equal to their resultant momentum, which has only an x component, say dM_x.

Thus

$$dM_x = mi_u du$$

That is

$$\int_0^\pi \rho u \cos\theta \, . \, 2\pi u^2 \sin\theta d\theta = i_u$$

In the velocity diagram of the electrons in the unit spatial volume the constancy (in a steady state) of the resultant momentum of the electrons with velocity less than u is due to a balance between several processes. The lateral motion with velocity C causes the value of ρ at any point in the velocity diagram to increase at the rate

$$- C \cos\theta \partial\rho_0/\partial u$$

(neglecting the ρ_1 term) and the motion of electrons through the faces of the unit spatial volume is causing ρ to increase at the rate

$$- u \cos \theta \partial \rho_0 / \partial x$$

Thus from these two causes the total momentum inside the sphere of radius u is increasing at the rate

$$- \int_0^u \int_0^\pi \left(C \frac{\partial \rho_0}{\partial u} + \frac{u \partial \rho_0}{\partial x} \right) \cos \theta \, . \, mu \cos \theta \, . \, 2\pi u^2 \sin \theta du d\theta$$

$$= - \frac{4\pi m}{3} \int_0^u \left(C u^3 \frac{\partial \rho_0}{\partial u} + u^4 \frac{\partial \rho_0}{\partial x} \right) du \quad . \quad (2.23)$$

The balancing process, collisions, is diminishing the momentum of electrons contained in the sphere at a rate

$$\int_0^u m u i_u du / l_m(u) \quad . \quad . \quad . \quad . \quad (2.24)$$

neglecting the contribution from the relatively few collisions in which the electrons move across the surface of the sphere.

Thus differentiating 2.23 and 2.24 with respect to u, it follows that

$$i_u = - \frac{4\pi}{3} C l_m(u) u^2 \frac{\partial \rho_0}{\partial u} - \frac{4\pi}{3} u^3 l_m(u) \frac{\partial \rho_0}{\partial x} \quad . \quad (2.25)$$

In evaluating

$$i = \int_0^\infty i_u du,$$

$$\int_0^\infty l_m(u) u^2 \, . \, \frac{\partial \rho_0}{\partial u} \, . \, du$$

may be replaced by

$$- \int_0^\infty \rho_0 \{ \partial (l_m(u) \, . \, u^2) / \partial u \} du$$

Thus, remembering that the number dn of electrons with velocities between u and $u + du$ is

$$4\pi u^2 \rho_0 du$$

and using a bar to signify mean values, it follows that the expression for transport, or the momentum equation, is

$$i = - \frac{1}{3} \frac{d}{dx} \overline{n u l_m(u)} + \frac{1}{3} \frac{eEn}{m} \overline{\left(\frac{2 l_m(u)}{u} + \frac{d l_m(u)}{du} \right)} . \quad (2.26)$$

The steady state drift velocity W_- is obtained by putting $dn/dx = 0$.

2.6 Energy Distribution Function

Consider now the velocity distribution of the electrons in a region (at some distance from the cathode) in which the distribution is constant in x. When all the collisions are elastic, and regarding the molecules as at rest, the small loss of energy of the electron is always positive. Thus if $h(F, u)$ is the fraction of the collisions, with initial velocity u in which the fraction of energy lost is greater than F, then, since $h(F, u)$ is practically zero when F is more than a very small fraction, the rate at which collisions transfer electrons across the surface of a sphere of radius u in the velocity diagram is practically

$$\frac{u}{l(u)} \cdot 4\pi u^2 \rho_0 \cdot \frac{u}{2} \int_0^1 h(F, u) dF \quad . \quad . \quad . \quad (2.27)$$

The integral

$$\int_0 h(F, u) dF$$

has a simple physical meaning, for, in collisions made by electrons with velocity u, the mean fractional loss of energy $\Delta(u)$ is given by

$$\Delta(u) = - \int_0^1 \frac{\partial}{\partial F} h(F, u) F \cdot dF$$

which, when integrated by parts, is

$$\int_0^1 h(F, u) dF.$$

Since the number of electrons inside the sphere of radius u is not changing with time, the collisional rate of transfer (2.27) across the surface of radius u must be balanced by the transfer due to the lateral motion with velocity C. This rate is

$$C \int_0^\pi \rho \cos \theta 2\pi u^2 \sin \theta d\theta = C i_u / u \quad . \quad . \quad (2.28)$$

Thus the balancing of 2.27 and 2.28 requires that

$$\frac{C i_u}{u} = \frac{u}{l(u)} \cdot 4\pi u^2 \cdot \rho_0 \frac{u}{2} \cdot \Delta(u) \quad . \quad . \quad . \quad (2.29)$$

Eliminating i_u between 2.25 (with $\partial \rho_0 / \partial x$ zero) and 2.29, it follows that

$$\frac{1}{\rho_0} \frac{d\rho_0}{du} = -\frac{3\Delta(u)u^3}{2C^2 l_m(u)l(u)}$$

and

$$\rho_0 = A \exp \int_0^u \frac{-3\Delta(u)u^3 du}{2C^2 l_m(u)l(u)} \quad . \quad . \quad . \quad (2.30)$$

In particular, if l, l_m, and Δ are all independent of u (elastic sphere collisions), this becomes if $l = l_m$

$$\rho_0 = A \exp\left(-3\Delta u^4/8C^2 l^2\right) \quad . \quad . \quad . \quad (2.31)$$

In its non-dimensional form this is

$$dN/N = 1 \cdot 04 y^{\frac{1}{2}} \exp\left(-0 \cdot 55 y^2\right) dy \quad . \quad . \quad (2.32)$$

where

$$y = \tfrac{1}{2}mu^2 / \overline{\tfrac{1}{2}mu^2}.$$

This formula was given by Druyvesteyn [62]. This distribution is considerably narrower than Maxwell's. In general, the distribution of electrons in electrical discharges is different from that given by 2.32, due to the following factors: (i) the variation of cross-section with velocity; (ii) the occurrence of inelastic collisions of electrons and molecules; and (iii) interaction of electrons.

Except for high current densities (e.g., in arc discharges), inter-action may be neglected; the occurrence of inelastic losses and the variation of cross-section with velocity can be taken into account in equation 2.30, but the integration can be made only if the cross-sections for elastic scattering, excitation, and ionization are all known as functions of u. The expression is therefore complicated, but the evaluation must be carried out for detailed calculation of the rate of ionization or excitation of electrons in gases. (Smit [251], Cahn [35], Abdelnabi and Massey [1].) This aspect will not be considered further here. Since the total effective cross-section is different for different gases, no simple general expression can be given; indeed, the distribution is likely to be different in different gases and even for different mean energies.

2.7 Drift Velocity: Mean Energy

For exact calculations the distribution must be known, nevertheless, for many purposes it is sufficient to consider the case in which the elastic cross-section Q is independent of u, and all u's are equal. In that part of the gas where the concentration is uniform, using equation 2.26 and putting

$$\partial l / \partial u = 0$$

gives the drift velocity W_- for electrons in the direction of the electric field in moderate fields, as

$$W_- = \frac{2eEl}{3m}\left(\frac{1}{u}\right) \quad . \quad . \quad . \quad . \quad (2.33)$$

This useful formula does not differ greatly from the exact formula based on known distributions. Davidson [54] has pointed out for the case of a distribution of velocities, however, that when l depends on u his correct equation 2.26 should be used, as considerable error is made if the average $\overline{(l/u)}$ or $l\overline{\left(\frac{1}{u}\right)}$ is used in equation 2.33.

Similarly, the value for the mean electron energy E_1 where

$$\overline{\tfrac{1}{2}mu^2} = \overline{E_1} = \int_0^\infty E_1 dn \Big/\! \int_0^\infty dn$$

may be found from the distribution, but when all u's are equal and l is constant, and using 2.33,

$$\overline{E}_1 = \frac{E}{p} \cdot \frac{l_1}{\sqrt{3\Delta}} \, \mathrm{eV} \quad . \quad . \quad . \quad (2.34)$$

where $l_1 =$ mean free path at a pressure of 1 mm. Hg and E is in V/cm. Values of E_1 given by this relation agree well with those measured for low fields by Townsend in his diffusion experiments [263]. In helium $l_1 = 0.05$ cm., and $\Delta = 2.73 \times 10^{-4}$, giving

$$\overline{E}_1 = 2\frac{E}{p} \cdot \mathrm{eV}$$

In the positive column [145] of helium E/p is 2V/cm. mm. Hg, so that

$$E_1 = 4 \, \mathrm{eV}$$

and is thus 100 times the mean energy ($\sim 1/27$ eV) of the gas atoms. Substitution of numerical values for e, u, m, and l in 2.33 gives $W_- \sim 10^7$ cm./sec. for electrons at practical values of E/p. For positive ions, owing to their larger mass, W_+ is $\sim 10^5$ cm./sec.

For positive ions of charge e the transport equation corresponding to equations 2.26 is

$$i_+ = -\frac{1}{3} L_+ U \frac{dn}{dx} + \frac{eL_+}{MU} En$$

where the numerical coefficient $\frac{2}{3}$ in equation 2.33 is replaced by unity; this is because for such particles the scattering is not uniform as it is for electrons. This leads to an approximate mobility formula

$$W_+ = \frac{eEL_+}{M} \overline{\left(\frac{1}{u}\right)} \quad . \quad . \quad . \quad . \quad (2.35)$$

2.8 Diffusion

If the concentration on one side of unit area in a gas is greater than that on the other, there is a net flow i atoms/sec. across the gas, where

$$i = -D \ \mathrm{grad} \ n \quad . \quad . \quad . \quad . \quad (2.36)$$

and D is the coefficient of diffusion. For particles of high velocity but low concentration diffusing in a gas of high concentration and negligible velocity, D is given by

$$D = \tfrac{1}{3}\overline{lu} \quad . \quad . \quad . \quad . \quad . \quad (2.37)$$

It follows that even when in thermal equilibrium with the gas atoms, owing to their greater l and u, D_- for electrons is 10^3 times greater than that D_+ for gas atoms or positive ions; in an electric field when the electron energy is higher D_- is even greater. Thus in a concentration gradient electrons tend to move away from the region of ionization and leave the slower positive ions behind.

It is interesting to note that for a Maxwellian distribution it follows from (2.35) and (2.37) that

$$W_+/D_+ = Ene/p$$

where p is the partial pressure of the ion gas. This equation has been used to determine the ionic charge.

2.8.1 *Diffusion from a Point Source.* Consider a total number of particles N released at the origin at time $t = 0$ in a gas. At a time t later these particles will be distributed at different vectorial distances $r_1, r_2, \ldots r_n$. The mean square distance is defined by

$$\overline{r^2} = \int_0^\infty \rho r^2 d\tau \bigg/ \int_0^\infty \rho d\tau \quad . \quad . \quad . \quad (2.38)$$

where ρ is the concentration of particles in volume element $d\tau$ distance r from the origin. Consider an elementary volume shell, then

$$d\tau = 4\pi r^2 dr$$

and the rate of decrease of particles = flux out from surface, so that

$$\left. \begin{aligned} -\frac{\partial}{\partial t}(\rho d\tau) &= -D\frac{\partial}{\partial r}\left(4\pi r^2\frac{\partial\rho}{\partial r}\right)dr \\ \frac{\partial\rho}{\partial t} &= D\left(\frac{2}{r}\frac{\partial\rho}{\partial r} + \frac{\partial^2\rho}{\partial r^2}\right) \end{aligned} \right\} \quad . \quad . \quad (2.39)$$

and

giving

$$\left. \begin{aligned} \rho/N &= \exp\left(-r^2/4Dt\right)/(4\pi Dt)^{3/2} \\ \overline{r^2} &= 6Dt \end{aligned} \right\} \quad . \quad (2.40)$$

and

This case and the case of cylindrical diffusion, for which

$$\overline{r^2} = 4Dt \; . \quad . \quad . \quad . \quad (2.41)$$

are of special interest in discharges, and equation 2.41 in particular is important in considering the lateral diffusion of ions from, say, a

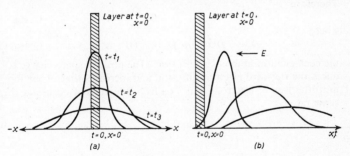

FIG. 2.6. Diffusion of an electron layer (a) in field-free space; (b) in an electric field

current through a gas, as it enables the cross-sectional area of the current to be estimated. They were also used by Perrin to evaluate Avogadro's number from Brownian movement.

2.8.2 *Change of Distribution with Distance.* Using 2.26 above, when u is the same for all electrons

$$\frac{\partial i}{\partial x} = -\frac{lu}{3}\frac{\partial^2\rho}{\partial x^2} + \frac{2leE}{3mu}\frac{\partial\rho}{\partial x} = -\frac{\partial\rho}{\partial t} \; . \quad . \quad (2.42)$$

Using equations 2.33 and 2.37 and putting $z = x - W_{-}t$

$$\frac{\partial \rho}{\partial t} = D_{-}\partial^2\rho/\partial z^2$$

so that

$$\rho = \frac{N}{\sqrt{4\pi D_{-}t}} \cdot \exp\left(-z^2/4Dt^2\right) \quad . \quad . \quad (2.43)$$

Thus the spatial distribution is that corresponding to simple diffusion at x_0 when x_0 moves with velocity W_{-}, and is illustrated in Fig. 2.6.

This result can be used to estimate the cross-sectional area of a spark-discharge current [143].

2.8.3 *Ambi-polar Diffusion*. The more rapid initial lateral diffusion of the electrons can leave a positive space charge due to positive ions, which in a steady current reduces the lateral electron diffusion. If the electron and positive-ion concentrations are nearly equal

$$i_r = -D_{-}\rho' - W_{-}\rho = -D_{+}\rho' + W_{+}\rho \quad . \quad (2.44)$$

where i_r is the (equal) electron and ion outward lateral current and ρ' means $\partial\rho/\partial r$.
Therefore

$$i_r = -D_a\rho' \quad . \quad . \quad . \quad . \quad . \quad (2.45)$$

where

$$D_a = (D_{-}W_{+} + D_{+}W_{-})/(W_{+} + W_{-}) \quad . \quad . \quad (2.46)$$

the coefficient of ambipolar diffusion. The positive space charge reduces the outward electron diffusion and increases that of the ions until the loss of electrons and ions from the current occurs at the same rate.

CHAPTER III

Fundamental Processes of Ionization and De-ionization

Ionization processes of significance in electrical breakdown may be conveniently classified as gas processes involving the collisions of electrons, ions, and photons with gas molecules, and electrode processes which take place at or near electrode surfaces. This chapter gives a brief survey of such processes. For a more detailed account the reader is referred to Massey and Burhop [173].

GAS PROCESSES

3.1 Single Electron Impact

When the kinetic energy $\frac{1}{2}mu^2$ of an electron in collision with a neutral gas molecule exceeds the ionization energy eV_i of the molecule, ionization can occur (see § 2.1), and, in general, a positive ion and two slow electrons result. The atom cross-section for this process is zero for electron energies equal to the ionization energy E_i of the molecule, but increases almost linearly at first, and then gradually with electron energy up to about 100 eV, and tends to fall off for higher energies. The rate of occurrence of this process is proportional to the concentration of the colliding electrons, i.e., the rate of ionization is directly proportional to the current.

3.2 Double Electron Impact

Ionization can also be produced by a relatively slow electron with energy less than the ionization energy in collision with a molecule which has been previously raised to an excited state E_e. Ionization can occur if

$$\frac{1}{2}mu^2 > E_i - E_e$$

An important case arises when E_e is a metastable level E_m, since the chance of a favourable collision is then greater, because of the relatively long lifetime of metastable states compared with that of other excited states. When the metastable molecules (or atoms) are first produced by impact of electrons from the current, then the rate of ionization in this double-impact process is proportional to the square of the current. In this way, experiment can help to distinguish between the action of this process and that of the single impact process (§ 3.1).

3.3 Ion–Atom Collisions

If the interaction between an ion and an atom takes place slowly, the internal motion of the system can gradually adjust itself throughout the collision to the gradually changing condition without any energy transition occurring and the collision is elastic. If the collision is very rapid and takes place in a time comparable with the period of the internal motion of the system, there will then be insufficient time for internal adjustment of the system to take place and an inelastic collision occurs, resulting in radiation or electron liberation [172]. The cross-section for the process will be correspondingly small. This conclusion appears to hold for simple atomic charge transfer, but the simplest molecular systems show wide discrepancies [108], and further experimental and theoretical work is necessary.

A large number of attempts have been made to detect the onset potential for ionization by ion–atom collision, but in general these investigations have yielded negative results. For example, the investigations of Sutton and Mouzon [255, 256], Beeck [14], and Varney [290] have indicated that positive ion energies $\gtrsim 300$ eV were necessary before any ionization could even be detected. Energies of this order are unlikely to occur in ordinary discharges at high pressures, and such an ionization process would consequently be of little significance. Recently, however, Horton and Millest [117] devised a sensitive method of detecting ionization which has shed new light on this question. They showed that normal helium atoms could ionize normal He atoms for energies > 49.4 eV; the maximum energy which could be transferred in such collisions was thus on classical theory 2×24.7 eV (the ionization energy of helium) (see § 2.3). This work indicates possibly that experimental apparatus previously used was not sufficiently sensitive to detect the effect looked for.

There is a dearth of experimental evidence on direct measurements of energies of positive ions in their own gas. Work done some years ago with argon appeared to show that even with $E/p = 150$ the mean agitational energy, although increasing with the field, was low (~ 0.2 eV), and further, the slightest trace of impurities reduced the ion energies to thermal energies as if ion clusters had been formed. Further experimental and theoretical work on the probability of ionization of gas molecules by positive ions is greatly needed.

Another type of collision is that in which charge transfer occurs. A valence electron of an atom is captured in collision by a positive ion which is thus neutralized. The reaction between slow neutral argon atoms and neon positive ions is represented by

$$A + Ne^+ \longrightarrow A^+ + Ne + \text{kinetic energy}$$

Kinetic energy equal to the difference between the potential energies $E_i(Ne)$ and $E_i(A)$ of the neon and argon ions is released, and can be distributed between the two particles. This type of collision can only be treated adequately using quantum mechanics, and the probability of the occurrence depends upon the difference of the potential energy of the two ions; the greater this difference, the lower the probability. From the Principle of Microscopic Reversibility it may be deduced also that the reverse process

$$A^+ + Ne \longrightarrow A + Ne^+$$

can occur only if the particles have a combined kinetic energy before collision exceeding $E_i(Ne) - E_i(A)$. The case of atoms A, B of the same element is also interesting:

$$A + B^+ \longrightarrow A^+ + B$$

Here no kinetic energy is required or released in the transfer process, and no momentum considerations are then involved. A resonance occurs, and the probability of the charge transfer in collision is a maximum.

There are important consequences of this effect. It is one of the reasons why it is difficult to produce a homogeneous beam of high-speed positive ions in a gas because charge transfer in collisions continually produces fast neutral atoms and slow ions. This effect is used as a means of producing fast atoms.

3.4 Excited Atom–Molecule Collision

An atom can return from a normal excitation level either directly or via other states, within times $\sim 10^{-8}$ sec. to the ground state, so releasing the energy E_e as one or more quanta of radiation. Owing to selection rule restrictions, the metastable level of an atom can be excited only by direct electron impact; return from it to the ground state requires an impact with another body. If no such body strikes the atom while in this state, the atom remains excited for a comparatively long time $\sim 10^{-1}$ sec. In such times, and with pressures ~ 1 mm. Hg, the atom can undergo some millions of collisions. On the other hand, when excited to an optical level the atom suffers few collisions, except when the gas pressure is extremely high ($\sim$ atmospheres), before returning to the ground state. The presence of metastable atoms can have considerable effect on the conductivity of a gas when it contains atoms of a different element with an ionization potential less than the potential corresponding to the metastable level of the gas atoms. In a collision between these two atoms the potential energy transferred from the metastable atom is now great enough to produce ionization of the other particle. This is a special case of a collision of the second kind, which can be of great importance in the conduction of electricity through gases. A typical collisional process of that kind is represented by a relation such as

$$Ne_m + A \longrightarrow Ne + A^+ + e$$

where Ne and Ne_m represent a normal and metastable neon atom respectively, A and A^+ a normal argon atom and its positive ion respectively, and e an electron. This process is known as the Penning effect [203]. Since the ionization potential of the common molecular gases such as oxygen, nitrogen, and hydrogen is about 15 eV, it is clear that collisions of the second kind can be very important in monatomic gases such as helium ($E_m \sim 20$ eV) and neon ($E_m \sim 16$ eV) because very slight traces of impurity enable collisions of the second kind to occur, and thus lead to increased ionization. The existence of the Penning effect is the reason why the highest degree of gas purity is desirable when investigating the electrical properties of the noble gases, helium, neon, and argon. At pressures ~ 1 mm. Hg a metastable atom can make about 10^8 collisions during its lifetime, and thus make about 100 collisions with a molecule of impurity which may be present in the main gases in a proportion as low as one part in a million.

3.5 Photo-ionization

A molecule in a ground state can be ionized by a photon of frequency ν provided $h\nu > E_i$, where h is Planck's constant. Experimental determination of the cross-section for this purpose in the common gases is difficult, partly on account of the high absorption of radiation of short wavelength ($\lesssim 900$ Å). The cross-section is generally significant only when $h\nu \simeq E_i$. The phenomenon was first investigated by Wiedemann [297] and by J. J. Thomson [260]. Work for air has been carried out by Cravath [48], Schneider [235], and more recently by Curtis [53], and by Weissler [292, 293, 294] and his colleagues in the United States, by Raether [209] in Germany, by Greiner [97] in Switzerland. Schneider, Weissler, and others all used a vacuum spectrograph with photographic plates; Curtis used a vacuum spectrograph with photo-electric cells. Schneider, Curtis, and Weissler measured the total absorption of the photons due to all causes, while Greiner and Raether investigated the electrons produced as a result of the photo-ionization, thus measuring more directly the cross-section for ionization. The experimental results so far published are not in good agreement, and accurate determinations of the cross-sections, especially for the common gases air, nitrogen, oxygen, and hydrogen, are greatly needed; and work is at present being done by Weissler on oxygen and nitrogen.

Photo-ionization can also occur in steps (see § 3.2); the process becomes important only for high concentration of excited atoms [118]. Ionization of Hg is possible by low-energy quanta ($\lambda >$ 2537 Å) producing two excited atoms which collide to form a molecular positive ion and a free electron.

3.6 Miscellaneous Processes

3.6.1 *Auto-Ionization*. In metal vapour auto-ionization can occur as follows. Two electrons in the same atom are first excited, and one may be released if the total potential energy of the excited atom then exceeds its ionization potential [248].

3.6.2 *Atom–Atom Collisions*. Again, two identical atoms in the ground state may become ionized in collisions if their relative velocity exceeds the value corresponding to twice their ionization energy. This process has been demonstrated experimentally and is in accordance with the classical collision laws (§ 2). Ionization can also be produced in atom–atom collision. The relative kinetic energy of the atom must be about twice the ionization energy, i.e. $\sim$30 eV, so that this process becomes significant only at very high gas temperatures (Saha [225, 226] process) such as obtain in arc discharges or in stellar atmospheres; it may usually be ignored in considering the early stages of breakdown of gases at ordinary temperatures.

3.7 De-Ionization

De-ionization can take place through the action of processes of recombination or attachment, as well as by the processes of diffusion and drift which have been discussed previously.

3.7.1 *Recombination*. In a gas containing positive ions and electrons there is a tendency for these to come together in collision and recombine to form neutral atoms. When an electron is captured it loses kinetic energy, which can be transferred to a third body or be emitted as a quantum of radiation. The transfer to a third body, if available, is the most probable process, the probability of emission as a photon being low. As a result there is, in general, little recombination in the body of the gas at low pressures in a discharge tube; recombination generally occurring at the walls, which act as the third body. Very high gas pressures render three-body collisions more probable, and recombination in the gas is then more likely to occur.

An ionization current in the gas is proportional to the electron density, consequently phenomena which are dependent on recombination, whether de-ionization or the emission of radiation, will then be proportional to the square of the current, and this fact is very useful in detecting the significance of recombination in any given case.

If the concentration of positive ions is n_+ and that of electrons n_-, the chance of an electron capture is proportional to $n_+ n_-$. Therefore $dn_-/dt = dn_+/dt = - Rn_+ n_-$, where R is called the coefficient of recombination. In many ionization phenomena n_- is nearly equal to n_+ $(= n)$, and $n_+ - n_-$ small compared with n. Therefore

$$dn/dt = - Rn^2,$$

where R is the coefficient of recombination. Integration gives

$$1/n_t - 1/n_0 = Rt$$

and this enables R to be obtained from measurements of the decay of electron density. This principle underlies most determinations of R [15, 16, 229, 230, 231, 232]. Such experiments are not easy, however; not only must the gas be extremely pure, but the existence of charge transfer and collisions of the second kind also make it difficult to know what kinds of particle are really involved. A further complication occurs with molecular gases owing to the added possibility of dissociation which introduces various contributions by which any excess energy can be redistributed [175].

3.7.2 *Attachment*. With his mass spectrograph, J. J. Thomson identified negative ions formed by the attachment of an electron to an atom or molecule. Gases with high attachment energies which form stable negative ions are the halogens, oxygen, sulphur, and various hydrocarbons. These elements have a slightly lower potential energy in the form of a negative ion than in the normal neutral state, and this is the condition for the formation of a negative ion. The energy difference between these two states is called the electron affinity, which energy is released on the formation of a negative ion. The monatomic gases do not form stable ions. The probability of attachment is influenced by factors similar to those concerning recombination, i.e., the presence of a third body, whether another colliding particle or one formed by molecular dissociation. Similarly the excitation of molecular vibration helps in the disposal of excess energy [171]. The principle of detailed balancing shows that for every process of electron attachment there exists a reverse process of detachment, but experimental data on detachment is more difficult to obtain than for attachment because of the difficulty of obtaining high concentrations of negative ions.

ELECTRODE PROCESSES

Electrons can be removed from solids to take part in electrical discharges by (*a*) providing them with sufficient kinetic energy to

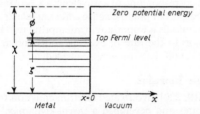

FIG. 3.1. Energy diagram of electrons in a metal

surmount the potential barrier at the surface of the solid, or (*b*) by reducing the height of, or thinning, the barrier so that the electrons can penetrate it and escape by virtue of their wave characteristics. Sufficient kinetic energy may be imparted by the application of heat, resulting in thermionic emission, or by the impact of light quanta of sufficient energy to cause photo-electric emission. Reduction and thinning of the barrier can be brought about by the application of strong electric fields to the surface, leading to so-called field emission. Again, electron emission from solids can be caused by the incidence of particles; those of main interest in electrical discharges being electrons, positive ions, metastable atoms, and neutral atoms.

To understand these processes of electron liberation [126] it is convenient to consider a metal as a box within which the potential energy of an electron is lower than that of one outside by an amount χ. In the box the electrons have kinetic energies which are distributed up to a maximum value ζ in accordance with the Fermi–Dirac statistics. It is customary to refer to the difference $(\chi - \zeta)$ as the work function ϕ of the metal, since $(\chi - \zeta)$ is the work necessary to remove an electron from the metal (see Fig. 3.1).

3.8 Photo-electric Emission

W. Hallwachs [105] established that the incidence of ultra-violet light upon a metal caused the emission of electrons. Einstein [74] suggested that light could be regarded as being made up of quanta, each of energy $h\nu$; moreover, it was assumed that the quanta transferred their energy *in toto* to the electrons in the metal. Hence, if $h\nu > \phi$ an electron at the Fermi level could escape with energy E_1 given by

$$E_1 = h\nu - \phi$$

This equation has been verified by Millikan [184]. For clean nickel surfaces, for example, with $\phi = 4\cdot5$ eV the threshold frequency $(= \phi/h)$ is that corresponding to a wavelength $\lambda = 2755$ Å. A knowledge of the efficiency of photo-electric emission (electrons/quantum) from various materials is important in attempting to relate the actual cathode emission to the rate of exciting collisions in the gas, and reliable experimental data are greatly needed.

3.9 Thermionic Emission

Richardson [219, 220] investigated electron emission from metals at high temperatures and developed a thermodynamical theory from

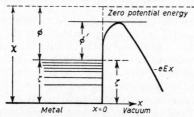

FIG. 3.2. Energy diagram when an electric field is applied

which he related the current density J to the absolute temperature T of the metal. He showed that

$$J = AT^{\frac{1}{2}} \exp\left(- \phi/kT\right),$$

where k is Boltzmann's constant, ϕ is the work function of the metal at an absolute temperature $T°$, and A is a constant having the dimension of current density. This equation, which yielded good agreement with experiment, was later modified by Richardson and by Dushman [67] to

$$J = AT^2 \exp\left(-\phi/kT\right)$$

Nordheim [193, 194] obtained the same formula by applying wave mechanics to the Sommerfeld model of a metal, showing that

$$J = A(1 - r)T^2 \exp\left(-\phi/kT\right),$$

where r is the probability that electrons which have sufficient energy to get over the barrier are reflected back. Owing to the predominance of the exponential term, it is not easy to distinguish experimentally between the different forms of the equation.

3.10 Schottky Emission

Under strong applied electric fields the work function is effectively reduced to

$$\phi' = \phi - e^{3/2}E^{\frac{1}{2}}.$$

Thus if I_0 is the emission for zero field at a temperature T, i.e., $I_0 = AT^2 \exp\left(-\phi/kT\right)$, then I_E, the current for a field E, is

$$I_E = I_0 \exp\left(e^{3/2}E^{\frac{1}{2}}/kT\right)$$

This relation which was derived by Schottky [242] has been shown to be valid over a wide range of temperatures and for fields up to 10^6 V/cm. by de Bruyne [33].

3.11 Field Emission

Calculations of the Schottky emission for $T = 293°$ K. (room temperature) and for values of $\phi \sim 4\cdot5$ eV (metals like Ni and W) show that the Schottky emission is negligible even when fields $\sim 10^6$ V/cm. are applied. However, experiment shows that under such fields electrodes *in vacuo* at room temperature do emit appreciable currents ($\sim\mu A$).

A wave mechanical treatment of the problem shows that electrons do not have to surmount the reduced potential barrier of height ϕ, but can by virtue of their wave properties tunnel through the potential barrier. This is known as the tunnel effect. Fowler and Nordheim [87] have considered the transparency of such a potential barrier to electrons when a strong electric field is applied to the pure metallic surface *in vacuo*, and have shown that the electron emission for a field E at the electrode surface is

$$I = \frac{e}{2\pi h} \cdot \frac{\zeta^{\frac{1}{2}} E^2}{(\zeta + \phi)\phi^{\frac{1}{2}}} \cdot \exp\left(-4k\phi^{3/2}/3E\right)$$

$$= \frac{38 \cdot 5 \times 10^{12} \zeta^{\frac{1}{2}} E^2}{(\zeta + \phi)\phi^{\frac{1}{2}}} \exp\left(-6 \cdot 8 \times 10^7 \phi^{3/2}/3E\right) \text{electrons/sec./cm.}^2.$$

With $\zeta = 5$ eV (value for base metals) and $\phi = 4 \cdot 5$ eV, a current $\sim \mu$A should require fields $E \sim 10^7$ to 10^8 V/cm. Work on field emission up to 1943 has been reviewed by Jenkins [124]. The most recent comprehensive work under conditions of very high vacua ($p \sim 10^{-10}$ mm. Hg) has been carried out by Dyke *et al.* [60, 61, 71].

In recent years experiment has shown that a field-dependent emission can apparently be obtained at fields which are one to two orders of magnitude less than this in the presence of surface contamination and gases. This can be of considerable significance in electrical breakdown, and will be considered in greater detail later.

3.12 Incidence of Positive Ions [1]

When a positive ion approaches a metallic cathode it may be: (i) reflected as an ion; (ii) reflected as an unexcited atom; (iii) reflected as an excited atom; (iv) cause sputtering of the surface; (v) cause electrons to be emitted (*a*) due to the kinetic energy given up on impact, and (*b*) due to a double process of metastable atom formation and radiation-less transition; or (vi) form a negative ion.

3.12.1 *Reflection.* Many positive ions incident on a surface will be scattered back with a loss of energy. Such reflected ions are observed at all angles of reflection, and the energy of the ions depends on the angle of reflection. The reflection coefficient r = (number reflected)/(number incident) increases with energy and lies between 0·1 and 0·8 for rare-gas ions for energies between 400 and 1,400 eV; for alkali ions $r \sim 0 \cdot 004$.

3.12.2 *Neutralization.* The field and energy levels when a positive ion of potential energy E_i is a distance a from the metal surface are as shown in Fig. 3.3.

If the atom has an unoccupied level E_e (either the ground state or an excited level) whose energy is equal to that of an occupied level E_{ei} in the metal, then a resonance transition of the electron may take place between the metallic level and the unoccupied atomic level. This transition has a high probability when the ion is very near the

---

[1] For detailed treatment see refs. 34, 173.

metal, because it occurs between two states of equal energy. The condition [198] for the ion to be reflected as an excited atom is obtained by equating the energy necessary for the extraction of the electron from the 'box' to the energy released when the electron falls to the E_i level in the atom, i.e.

$$\chi - E_{el} = E_i - E_e;$$

and

$$\chi > E_i - E_e > \phi$$

is the condition for the positive ion to be reflected as a neutral atom. Reflection as a metastable atom is a special case of the reflection as

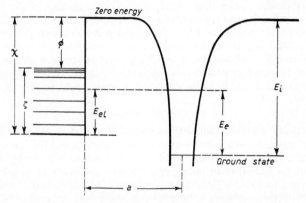

FIG. 3.3. Energy diagram of a positive ion near a metal

an excited atom. For example, for a He$^+$ ion ($E_i = 24 \cdot 47$ eV, $E_m = 19 \cdot 77$ eV) near a molybdenum surface ($\phi = 4 \cdot 3$ eV; $\chi = 14$ eV), the transition is possible, since $24 \cdot 47 - 19 \cdot 77 > 4 \cdot 3$. On the other hand, for an A$^+$ ion near Mo, $E_i = 15 \cdot 69$ eV; $E_m = 11 \cdot 49$ eV, and $(E_i - E_m) = 4 \cdot 2 < \phi = 4 \cdot 3$ eV, and the reaction is not possible. Now the level in helium for which $E_0 = 19 \cdot 77$ eV is metastable, so that the helium atom formed in the process will be metastable. Oliphant [197] did obtain metastable helium atoms by this method.

If the excited atom itself collides with the metal a transition may occur in which a second metal electron is liberated by the energy released when the excited atom returns to the ground state. If E_{el} is the initial kinetic energy of the electron in the metal, then

$$E_e = \chi - E_{el} + E_f > 0,$$

where E_f is the kinetic energy of the electron after liberation.

3.12.3 *Sputtering.* The impact of positive ions on a solid surface can cause sputtering, in which atoms are ejected from the surface as a result of the impact. For reviews of experimental and theoretical work see Massey and Burhop [173], and also Ecker and Emeleus [73].

3.12.4 *Ejection of Electrons.*

(a) *Due to kinetic energy.* The impact of high-energy positive ions on a cathode surface has been considered by Kapitza [127] to give rise to intense local heating and so lead to the thermionic emission of electrons. Oliphant and Moon [198] found that the energy distribution of electrons produced by positive ions was that to be expected if the process was in fact thermionic. This suggestion could also account for the fact that positive ions at grazing incidence produce more electrons than those at normal incidence with the same energy.

(b) *Due to impact of slow ions.* A positive ion approaching a metal surface with thermal velocity ($\sim 10^5$ cm./sec.) can become an excited atom by being neutralized in a transition between states of equal energy (see § 3.12.2). The transition is most likely to take place when

$$\phi = E_i - E_e$$

giving an excited atom with potential energy $E_e = (E_i - \phi)$. If neutralization takes place within 10^{-7} cm. of the metal the ion may collide with the metal within 10^{-12} sec. This time is probably too short for radiation to occur, and the atom probably gives up its energy to a metallic electron in a collision of the second kind: if this electron thus acquires a total energy $> \chi$ it will be emitted with energy

$$E = E_i - 2\phi$$

Thus if an excited atom of ionizing potential E_i is incident upon a surface of work function ϕ then provided

$$E_i > 2\phi$$

an electron will be ejected.

A fast-moving ion may penetrate the potential barrier before capturing an electron, to form a transient excited atom of energy E_i which would give up its energy instantaneously to a second electron, giving a normal unexcited atom and a high-energy electron which could escape from the metal. The energy relation for this transition is clearly

$$E_f = E_i - \phi$$

if the second electron is at the top Fermi level.

There is considerable direct experimental evidence [173] to show that slow positive ions are able to produce emission of electrons from metals. The data, however, are not all consistent, but this is very likely due to the fact that the emission is very sensitive to the state of the cathode surface; oxide, gas, or tarnish layers having considerable influence. Taking extensive precautions to ensure clean surfaces, Hagstrum [101, 102, 103] has determined the average number of electrons emitted per single positive ion for He^+, Ne^+, Ar^+, Kr^+, and Xe^+, finding a value of about 0·3 for He^+, for instance.

3.13 Incidence of Metastable and Normal Atoms

3.13.1 *Metastable Atoms*. Metastable atoms incident on a surface may: (i) be reflected; (ii) eject electrons provided $E_m > \phi$; (iii) be ionized, i.e., lose an electron to the metal and so form a positive ion provided $\phi \geqslant E_i - E_m$; (iv) be repelled as a negative ion, provided it is an electro-negative metastable atom.

3.13.2 *Normal Atoms*. A normal atom incident on a surface may: (i) be reflected; (ii) eject an electron if it has a sufficiently high kinetic energy; (iii) be ionized; (iv) be reflected as a negative ion.

3.13.3 *Formation of Negative Ions*. The potential-energy diagram is similar to Fig. 3.3, when the ground state of the atom now represents the ground state of an atom of electron affinity A. It can form a negative ion if

$$\chi = E_{el} + A$$

In order to remove an electron of initial kinetic energy E_{el} in the metal by the impact of excited atoms of electron affinity A, the condition

$$\chi - E_{el} = E + A > \phi$$

must be satisfied, for if $E_e + A < \phi$, then there would be no electron which had initially enough kinetic energy to make the transition because there are normally no electrons above the top Fermi level. Thus

$$\chi > E_e + A > \phi$$

is the condition for the formation of a negative ion by this means. If the atom is in the ground state the condition reduces to

$$\chi > A > \phi$$

The only case in which this condition is likely to be satisfied is that of a halogen atom incident on a clean alkali-metal surface.

CHAPTER IV

Breakdown in Static Uniform Fields at Lower Gas Pressures (pd ≤ 150 mm. Hg cm.)

4.1 The Problem

When a potential difference is established between, say, parallel-plate electrodes in a gas, the gas behaves as an insulator unless the potential exceeds a certain definite value, which is called the sparking or breakdown potential. In practice, this potential V_s is sharply defined; the gas insulates well at a potential only a few volts less than V_s. It is a matter of common observation that when the applied potential V is equal to or greater than V_s the insulation breaks down, a flash occurs, and a large current can pass if the circuit conditions permit, i.e., if the source of potential has a low impedance. If no initial electrons are provided, a spark does not occur even when V attains V_s; but in practice ionization due to natural radioactivity or cosmic rays eventually provides initiatory electrons. In the succeeding breakdown discharge, high current-density can be obtained, depending upon the gas pressure and distance between the plates, the electrodes can become heated, and almost a complete short-circuit of the source can be produced. The appearance of the discharge depends upon the conditions; in general, the lower the pressure, the wider is the glow produced. In the initial phase of the breakdown, the potential V across a gap is high ($= V_s$), but falls as the current increases to produce a glow with $V = V_g$; the potential can fall further to the arc value ($= V_a$) if sufficient thermionic or field emission of electrons occurs at the cathode. Once the breakdown current in a gas has begun to rise rapidly to significant magnitude, it is clear that the potential across the electrodes must depend upon the characteristic of the external circuit. Moreover, high current densities can themselves introduce further ionization phenomena, such as Saha ionization, thermionic emission from a cathode hot-spot, space-charge field intensification, especially at the cathode; and other phenomena usually associated with established discharges. The high current densities at the electrodes produced in the final phase of complete breakdown can produce evaporation of the electrode material. The sequence of events is approximately indicated in Fig. 4.1; the time of voltage collapse being very short ($\lesssim 10^{-7}$ sec.).

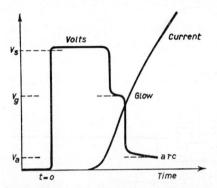

FIG. 4.1. Schematic diagram of voltage–time and current–time relationships during the development of a discharge

The physical problem is to account for the development of the ionization in an electric field from a small number of necessary initiatory electrons up to any specified final current, in terms of fundamental electronic, atomic, and ionic collision processes in the gas and electrode surface phenomena (Chapter III). In seeking an explanation of the cause of the spark in terms of the fundamental physics of atomic collisions, it is important first to consider the growth of ionization producing the transition of the gas from its completely insulating state to one in which the current can rise to a high value, depending on the external circuit. The added complication due to the rapid increase in current density leading to a low-voltage arc can be considered as a separate problem of established electrical discharges governed by space charges [144].

Much early work in this field was carried out at the Cavendish Laboratory, Cambridge, by J. J. Thomson and J. S. Townsend, who investigated the development of ionization in gases [247, 261, 262, 269, 264]. The work was carried out at low pressures with potentials $\lesssim 1{,}000$ V. Typical experimental arrangements used by Townsend and others are shown in Fig. 4.2. A is the anode and C the cathode of a parallel-plate gap at separation d, mounted in an envelope and connected to vacuum and gas systems. A steady initial electron current I_0 is produced from the cathode by irradiation through a quartz window W with ultra-violet light from a constant source S; the radiation can be arranged to pass through small holes in the anode. The electrode separation d can be varied by, for example, using a

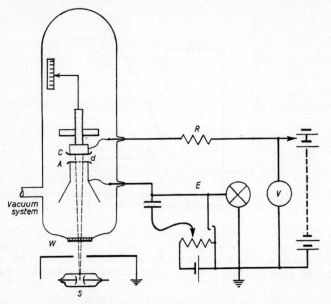

FIG. 4.2.   Ionization chamber and measuring circuit

screw mounting for the cathode, which can be rotated by an external magnet; alternatively, a metal bellows can be used. The whole apparatus is enclosed in a glass envelope with arrangements for outgassing and electrode cleaning. C can be connected through a resistance R to a source of steady potential V, such as a battery of accumulators, and A connected to earth through an instrument capable of measuring currents in the range 10^{-13}–10^{-7} A, such as an electrometer valve or a quadrant electrometer E.

4.2 Ionization Growth in Uniform Fields

When electrons and ions move through a gas in a uniform field E their mean energies attain equilibrium values dependent on the ratio

E/p (§ 2.7). Thus, in order to investigate how the current growth depends on factors such as the space through which the electrons move,

Gas			E/p	p	α	ω/α
Air	.	.	350	1	5·26	0·0028
N_2	.	.	165·3	2·48	4·13	0·00426
H_2	.	.	73·5	4·1	2·42	0·0095

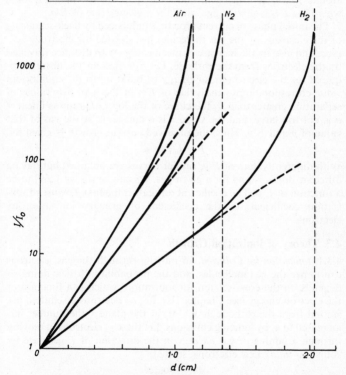

FIG. 4.3. Typical log $(I/I_0),d$ curves for air, nitrogen, and hydrogen at low gas pressures

or the nature of the electrode system, it is essential to maintain the mean energies of the electrons and ions constant and to measure the current I as a function of gap distance d; i.e., the ratio E/p must be maintained constant. This condition is the essential basis of this kind

D

of experimental investigation. It follows that in order to be able to specify the field exactly, it is necessary that the current density should be so small that the space charge does not disturb the field; hence these experiments are usually carried out with currents in the range 10^{-15}–10^{-7} A. Comprehensive measurements of the ionization current I have been made in a large number of different gases [65, 66, 223, 266]. Typical curves [11, 264] obtained for the common diatomic gases, air, nitrogen, and hydrogen, are given in Fig. 4.3, where $\log I/I_0$ is plotted against d for a given value of E/p.

The initial phase of current growth is influenced by back-scattering of the electrons by the gas molecules just outside the electrode surface; and also by the increase of mean energy with distance travelled by the electrons from the cathode. Let d_1 represent the distance required for the electron mean energy to build up to the equilibrium value corresponding to the value of E/p in the gap. For values of separation greater than d_1 the curve of the log I, d graph is linear if d is not too large, and the slope α is a constant for the gas at that value of p and E/p. Thus, the observed current growth is given by

$$I = I_0 \exp \alpha d$$

With different values of E/p, similar curves are obtained but having different slopes α, and for a given gas, α/p can be shown [269] to be a function of E/p. The coefficient α is called the first Townsend ionization coefficient, or the coefficient of primary ionization by electrons.

4.3 Theory of Ionization Growth

4.3.1 *Ionization by Collision*. In moving through the gas, electrons can ionize the gas molecules, and the probability of their doing so depends on the cross-section for ionization, which is a function of the electron energy (see Chapter III). Let n_0 electrons be emitted per second from the cathode at $x = 0$; at the plane x the number has increased to n_x by ionizing collisions. Let these n_x electrons in moving through a lamina of gas dx at x in the direction of E generate by collisions $\alpha n_x dx$ new electrons, so that

$$dn_x = \alpha n_x dx$$

The number n_d of electrons which strike the anode at $x = d$ is $n_0 \exp \alpha d$, and such a group of electrons is called an avalanche. It follows [269] that the total electron current I at the anode is given by—

$$\left. \begin{array}{l} I = I_0 \exp \alpha d \\ \log I/I_0 = \alpha d, \end{array} \right\} \quad \cdots \quad (4.1)$$

where I_0 is the initial electron current leaving the cathode. The co-efficient α can be related to the fundamental atomic data as follows. The total number of ionizations per second made by a group $\rho(u)du$ of electrons is $\rho(u) . Q_i(u) . u, du$ (see Chapter II, §§ 2.5, 2.6); and the total number of ionizations made by all the N electrons traversing a lamina dx of gas is

$$dx \int_0^\infty \rho(u) . Q_i(u) . u . du/W_- = N . \alpha . dx$$

where W_- is given by equations 2.26 or 2.33 in Chapter II. It readily follows that

$$\alpha/p = f(E/p)$$

There is thus no difficulty in principle in finding the function f by relating α to fundamental atomic properties, and many attempts [146] have been made to do so. The main difficulty in practice in calculating α is that of knowing sufficiently accurately the energy-distribution function $\rho(u)$ and the cross-section term $Q_i(u)$. An early formula due to Townsend [270], obtained by ignoring the distribution and ionization probability functions and assuming that all electrons which exceeded V_i in energy ionize, is

$$\alpha/p = A \exp \{- B/(E/p)\}$$

This is often useful in calculations for many gases. For instance, when $A = 5$, $B = 13$, this formula agrees well with the values of α in hydrogen measured by Ayres for $100 < E/p < 600$ V/cm.mm.Hg. More rigorous calculations have been made in recent years for various gases [173].

4.3.2 *Action of Secondary Ionization Processes on the Spatial Growth of Current.* The graphs in Fig. 4.3 are practically straight initially, but curve upwards at the larger values of d, finally becoming vertical at $d = d_s$. It is observed that just when d attains these values of d_s the breakdown flash occurs. For values of $d < d_s$ the complete form of these growth curves is given within the experimental error by the relation

$$I = I_0 \exp \alpha d/\{1 - C(\exp \alpha d - 1)\} \quad . \quad . \quad (4.2)$$

where α and C are constant when E/p is constant at a given p, as can be seen from Table I for air [271].

This table shows that with appropriate values for α and C, the growth of current is given by equation (4.2), and also that α/p and C are the same when E/p is the same. C is the second Townsend coefficient.

In order to elucidate its physical significance, it is reasonable to assume that C represents some process of ionization in addition to the α process, thus making the total ionization in the avalanche greater than that due to α alone. That the introduction of a secondary ionization process can predict an ionization growth curve of the

TABLE I

Air: $p = 1$ mm. Hg; $E = 350$ V/cm.; $\alpha = 5\cdot25$; $C = 0\cdot0027$

d cm. .	0·2	0·4	0·6	0·8	1·0	1·1
I obs. .	2·86	8·3	24·2	81	373	2250
exp αd .	2·86	8·2	23·4	66·5	190	
Equation 4.2	2·86	8·3	24·8	80	380	2180

Air: $p = 2$ mm. Hg; $E = 700$ V/cm.; $\alpha = 10\cdot5$; $C = 0\cdot0027$

d cm. .	0·1	0·2	0·3	0·4	0·5
I obs. .	2·9	8·3	23·8	80	374
Equation 4.2	2·87	8·3	24·6	80	380

same form as that observed, which follows equation 4.2, can be seen from the following considerations.

Assume that the electron–molecule collisions in the electron avalanche can, owing to the action of photons or positive ions produced by those collisions, produce a secondary electron emission from the cathode. Let n_x electrons, by traversing the gas layer dx at x, have this secondary effect of causing the emission of $\omega n_x dx$ electrons from the cathode, in addition to the primary ionization which produces $\alpha n_x dx$ electrons in the gas lamina dx.

Let $n_0 =$ initial photo-electric emission from cathode,

$n_0' =$ total electron emission from cathode (i.e., including secondary emission), and

$n_0'' =$ number leaving the cathode resulting from the avalanche alone.

Now $n_x = n_0 \exp \alpha x$,

and $n_0 = \int_0^d \omega n_0' \exp \alpha x \, dx$

$= (\omega/\alpha) n_0' (\exp \alpha d - 1)$

The total emission from the cathode is

$$n_0' = n_0 + n_0''$$
$$= n_0 + (\omega/\alpha)n_0'(\exp \alpha d - 1),$$

therefore

$$n_0 = n_0'\{1 - (\omega/\alpha)(\exp \alpha d - 1)\}.$$

The total number n_d of electrons at the anode is $n_0' \exp \alpha d$, so that

$$n_d = n_0 \exp \alpha d/\{1 - (\omega/\alpha)(\exp \alpha d - 1)\}. \quad . \quad (4.3)$$

which is of the same form as equation 4.2. Thus, $C(= \omega/\alpha)$ can represent a secondary ionization process such as electron emission from the cathode caused by incidence of either photons or positive ions (or both) from the avalanche [279].

4.4 Possible Secondary Processes: Definition of Coefficients

(i) *Secondary emission due to incidence of positive ions.* The production of $n_x \alpha dx$ new electrons at a lamina at x involves the production also of $n_x \alpha dx$ new positive ions. Let these ions produce at the cathode $\gamma n_x \alpha dx$ secondary electrons. The coefficient γ is defined as the number of electrons liberated from the cathode per single ionizing collision in the gas, and is therefore not dependent on the value of the current but depends on the cathode surface.

(ii) *Photo-electric emission.* When n_x electrons pass through a lamina dx of gas they excite molecules and produce $\alpha' n_x dx$ photons, a fraction θ (depending upon gap geometry and gas absorption) of which will fall on the cathode and produce

$$f\theta\alpha' n_x dx = \delta n_x dx$$

electrons. Thus δ is equivalent to ω in 4.3 above, and the number of photo-electrons emitted from the cathode per ionizing collision in the gas is thus δ/α. Absorption of photons in the gas may be neglected at low pressures. The total electron emission ω/α from the cathode due to positive ions and photons per ionizing collision in the gas is $\gamma + \delta/\alpha$. The photons may, however, undergo resonance fluorescence before reaching the cathode [42], and this would increase the time which elapses before the photons reach the cathode and produce photo-electrons.

(iii) *Gas ionization by positive ions.* In the early work still another form of ionization was considered, namely, that due to the direct ionization of neutral atoms by positive ions. This process can be described by a coefficient β, when

$$dn_x = \beta p_x dx$$

p_x being the concentration of positive ions at x. There is still a dearth of reliable experimental data on this process [173].

(iv) *Cathode emission due to incidence of excited atoms.* Excited atoms quickly return to the ground state, so hardly survive motion through the gas. Metastable atoms, on the other hand, travel by diffusion through the gas, and on reaching the cathode can produce secondary electrons. This action is similar to the photo-electric effect, except that the transport of energy to the cathode is slower, and the process can be represented by a coefficient ε/α of same dimensions as δ/α.

(v) *Stepwise ionization.* This occurs when either electrons or photons ionize already excited gas atoms: electrons or photons of energy given by

$$\tfrac{1}{2}mu^2 \text{ or } h\nu \geqslant E_i - E_e$$

are necessary. The ionization rate depends on the number of excited neutral atoms and on the number of colliding electrons or photons. Spontaneous rapid return of excited atoms to the ground state makes the population of excited atoms negligible. The ionization rate depends on the square of the electron concentration, and this would make the secondary coefficient depend on the value of the current.

(vi) *Photo-ionization.* The experimental cross-sections [292] indicate that at low pressures the influence of photo-ionization on the growth of current can usually be ignored. At higher pressures $\gtrsim 760$ mm. Hg, however, the process can be important, and therefore has to be quantitatively examined.

4.5 Growth of Current when All the Secondary Processes β, γ, δ, and ε Act at the Same Time

Assume that the initial electrons from the cathode quickly attain the mean energies corresponding to the value of E/p in the gap, so that all the various ionization coefficients, α, β, γ, δ, and ε are constant. The coefficient δ can, in the steady state, include ε due to diffusion of metastable atoms. The normally excited atom concentration will be low. Let suffix $-$ refer to electrons, and $+$ to ions. The continuity equations are

$$- dI_+/dx = dI_-/dx = \alpha I_- + \beta I_+$$

$$I_+ + I_- = \text{Total current } I$$

$$\therefore \quad dI_-/dx = \beta I + (\alpha - \beta)I_-$$

Integrating and using the boundary condition,

$$I_+(d) = 0$$

it can be shown that

$$L = $$

$$\frac{I_-(1 - \beta/\alpha) \exp \alpha d}{\exp \beta d \left[\left(1 - \frac{\beta}{\alpha} + \frac{\beta \delta d}{\alpha} \right) - \left(\frac{\exp \alpha d}{\exp \beta d} - 1 \right) \left\{ \gamma + \frac{\delta}{(\alpha - \beta)} + \frac{\beta}{\alpha}(1 - \delta d) \right\} \right]} \qquad (4.4)$$

Experimental data on the growth [148] of ionization currents in various gases show that, in general, β/α, βd, and δd are small compared with unity; thus equation 4.4 is practically indistinguishable from 4.3, where, neglecting terms of the second order,

$$\omega = \beta + \alpha \gamma + \delta + \varepsilon \quad . \quad . \quad . \quad (4.5)$$

Further, it also follows that each secondary coefficient β, $\alpha\gamma$, δ, or ε acting alone or in a linear combination leads to a growth equation of the same analytical form as 4.3. Consequently, it is not possible to elucidate the particular secondary process or processes which may be significant in any given case, simply from the form of the observed ionization growth curve, because all the processes, whether acting singly or in any combination, lead to a growth curve of the same form, which is that of equation 4.3. The significant secondary processes can only be effectively distinguished, therefore, by experiments of a different kind, and these will be discussed below.

It may be pointed out here, however, that the form of the log I, d growth curve for any given gas depends on the value of ω/α. For example, in helium [284, 285], ω/α is large (~ 0.1) and the linear section of the log I, d curve is very small; in CO_2, on the other hand, ω/α is small [265] ($\sim 4 \cdot 10^{-5}$), the linear section is large, and the final upcurving as d approaches d_s is sharp, as shown in Fig. 4.4.

When the only significant secondary process is that of positive ions producing secondary electron emission from the cathode, then equation 4.4 has the well-known form of

$$I = I_0 \exp \alpha d / \{1 - \gamma(\exp \alpha d - 1)\} \quad . \quad . \quad (4.6)$$

and similarly for the other separate secondary processes: β/α, δ/α, etc.

It will be noticed that in the above analysis of the action of various kinds of secondary processes, that of photo-ionization of the gas was omitted. As stated above, at low gas pressures this process is generally not important compared with other processes in uniform static fields. The full analysis is complicated, and is therefore omitted at this stage; later, in considering growth of ionization at high pressures in Chapter V, the process cannot be ignored, and the analysis is there given. It can be stated here, however, that when this process is not predominant and acts with others, then it may be described by

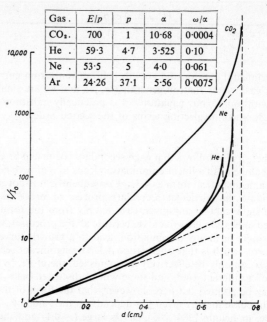

Gas .	E/p	p	α	ω/α
CO_2 .	700	1	10·68	0·0004
He .	59·3	4·7	3·525	0·10
Ne .	53·5	5	4·0	0·061
Ar .	24·26	37·1	5·56	0·0075

FIG. 4.4. Ionization growth curves in different gases, showing how the shape depends on the value of ω/α.

a coefficient η, similar to β, and therefore satisfying equations 4.3 and 4.5 when a term η is added.

In the above analysis it was assumed that the distance d through which the initial electrons from the cathode must travel in order to acquire the constant mean energy was negligible compared with the gap d. At low values of E/p, however, this is not the case, and it is found experimentally that, for instance, the growth of ionization currents in monatomic gases, such as neon and helium measured by Townsend and McCallum [284, 285], and in argon measured by Kruithoff and Penning [137] at low pressures, is described by putting $(d - d_1)$ for d in equation 4.2, i.e.,

$$I = I_0 \exp \alpha(d - d_1)/[1 - (\omega/\alpha)\{\exp \alpha(d - d_1) - 1\}]$$

The coefficients α and ω are functions of the field and the derivation of 4.3 assumes that the field in the gap is uniform and that the space charge of the current produces no significant change in α or ω. However, if I_0 and therefore I is sufficiently high, both α and ω can be affected by field distortion due to space charge [273].

It has also been assumed that no electron emission from the cathode occurs other than that due to external radiation or to the incidence of ions or photons from the electron avalanche. This assumption is justified for fields $\lesssim 10^4$ V/cm., but may not be justified for higher fields, which can produce emission from electrodes at room temperature (see § 6.1 below).

4.6 The Sparking Distance and Sparking Potential

4.6.1 *Sparking Criterion.* When $d < d_s$, I is proportional to I_0. If the original irradiation of the gap is cut off, I_0 becomes zero, and the total current I also ceases. However, from the form of the equation 4.3 it follows that when

$$1 - (\omega/\alpha)(\exp \alpha d_s - 1) = 0 \quad . \quad . \quad (4.7)$$

then $I \longrightarrow \infty$ as $d \longrightarrow d_s$, always assuming E/p is still constant. For any value of ω/α, however small, it is always possible to find a value of d_s which satisfies this relationship. When d_s is found at a particular value of E/p, $V (= Ed_s)$ can then be calculated. This distance d_s at which the current can increase very greatly can be regarded as the sparking or breakdown distance at the given value of E/p, so that $V = Ed_s$ is then the sparking potential. The value V as given by Ed_s, where d_s is the solution of the criterion (4.7), can thus be calculated by measuring α and ω/α directly from the growth of pre-breakdown ionization currents remote from the breakdown condition, and substituting these values in the criterion 4.7. The value V so obtained can then be compared with the potential V_s at which the breakdown is observed actually to occur. This has been done for many of the common gases such as air, H_2, N_2, CO_2, He, and Ne; Table II gives an example of experimental data obtained with CO_2 and air [272].

TABLE II

Gas	E	p	α	ω/α	d_s	V calculated	V_s observed
CO_2 .	1,400	2	21·24	0·0084	0·369	516	517
Air .	1,400	8	16·47	0·013	0·431	603	603

The agreement is satisfactory and implies that with the small initial currents ($\sim 10^{-12}$ A) used α and ω/α are constant, i.e., no significant distortion of the field was occurring even when approaching the sparking condition. Thus, the mechanism setting the breakdown criterion is the same as the mechanism of the growth of ionization current prior to breakdown, of which growth the transition is a natural development. Equation 4.7 is the Townsend criterion for breakdown in uniform static fields.

4.6.2 *The Physical Significance of the Criterion.* The current cannot continually increase without limit when $V = V_s$, because no practical source can supply the power to maintain V constant; equation 4·7 was derived from 4·3 on the assumption that E, α, and ω/α were constants. The physical interpretation of equation 4.7 is as follows.

If d_s satisfies the relationship 4.7, it follows from 4.7 that I can be finite even when I_0 is zero. It is easy to see that this condition 4.7 is really a mathematical statement of a replacement condition; viz., that the ionization processes in the gas are such that they replace, by generation in the gas or at the cathode, the electrons leaving the cathode and drawn to the anode. For instance, when n_0 electrons leave the cathode, $n_0(\exp \alpha d - 1)$ positive ions are created in the gap, and these on incidence on the cathode produce $\gamma n_0(\exp \alpha d - 1)$ new electrons. When 4.7 is satisfied the number of these new electrons is equal to the original n_0, which had been drawn away and afterwards pass into the anode. Consequently, it follows that the current in the gap is self-maintained at the particular value I obtaining when the irradiation of the cathode ceases and I_0 is reduced to zero. This is a physical condition which can be realized in the laboratory. Thus, the mathematical criterion represented by equation 4.7 represents a condition the physical significance of which is that when $d = d_s$ and $V = V_s$, then it is possible to have

$$\left.\begin{array}{l} I \text{ finite when } I_0 = 0, \text{ and} \\ V_s \text{ independent of } I \text{ when this is small} \\ \text{enough not to distort the field} \end{array}\right\} \qquad . \quad (4.8)$$

On this view, the sparking or breakdown potential V_s can be defined as the potential difference, independent of the current, which just maintains a small current. This physically specifies the breakdown criterion, and is unrelated to the attainment of infinitely large currents.

It is now possible to see why V_s is the static sparking potential below which breakdown cannot occur, and therefore why this quantity is so important in the theory of electrical discharges. When $V < V_s$, or $d < d_s$, I is always proportional to I_0, becoming zero when I_0 is zero; the current is steady in time and cannot exceed that value given by equation 4.3. As soon as $d = d_s$, or $V = V_s$, a current of any value small enough not to distort the field can just maintain itself with no further provision of initiatory electrons, as long as the potential V_s is maintained. It also follows that if the applied voltage V exceeds V_s, even by an infinitesimal amount, then E/p is correspondingly increased, with resultant increase in α. Consequently, the current I can now more than just maintain itself, and is thus bound to increase in time. The dynamics of this phase, which eventually leads to the collapse of the applied voltage, will be discussed below in Chapter VIII. It must be emphasized at this stage, however, that consideration of the increase of current with time must be made on the basis of the solution of the continuity equation for electron density as a function of time: the static equations 4.1 and 4.4 no longer apply, as they are steady-state relations. Considerations of the initial phase of the temporal growth of current just after the condition $V = V_s$, or $d = d_s$, is satisfied can give important information concerning the influence of the primary and secondary processes α and ω/α in the ionization growth and also indicate whether the field E remains undistorted even when $V > V_s$, but $V - V_s$ is still small, i.e., in the immediate neighbourhood of the breakdown condition when the transition occurs from the insulating to the conducting states.

Consider now the practical realization of this criterion 4.7. A saturated diode introduced in series with the gap can restrict the current to any specified value, enabling V to be measured for the various values of I, and therefore the functional dependence of I on V to be found. Fig. 4.5 gives an example of such a curve obtained in hydrogen by C. Grey Morgan and E. Jones at Swansea, showing that I is independent of V_s over a wide range up to 20 μA, the range itself depending on p and d.

The experimental determination of such curves is, however, not easy. In the first place, the diode will not be completely saturated, and a change of voltage will produce a small change of current; secondly, the nature of the cathode in general determines the maintenance condition mainly through the action of γ and δ effects. The micro-geometry and micro-state of the cathode then greatly influence the stability of the current, and these can change while current passes unless the cathode surface is clean, smooth, and degassed. This effect becomes more important at higher pressures because of the

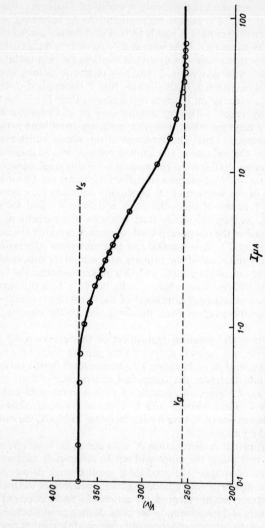

Fig. 4.5. Current-voltage characteristic at breakdown, showing attainment of a stable state when a glow discharge is set up. Copper electrodes in hydrogen, $p = 11.8$ mm.Hg. $d = 0.2$ cm.

localization of the current due to various causes, such as the diminution of lateral diffusion. This makes it extremely difficult to obtain static V, I characteristic curves at high gas pressures.

As the current is allowed to increase further, the total potential falls, but only to a certain limit, at which a glow appears near the anode [247]. This phase at low pressures is called a glow discharge, and the voltage is called V_g, the discharge-maintenance potential as indicated in Fig. 4.1. Thus, by interposing a controlling device for the current, it is possible to examine slowly the phenomena which can occur almost instantaneously ($\lesssim 10^{-7}$ sec.) if the current is not so controlled.

4.7 Paschen's Law

The dependence of the breakdown potential V_s on the product pd_s was first established experimentally by de la Rue and Muller [224]; later, Paschen [201] concluded, from an extensive study of air, CO_2, and H_2 over a range of values of pd_s, that V_s is a function ϕ (pd_s) of the product pd_s only. This result is known as Paschen's Law, and Carr [36] confirmed its validity for a number of different gases for values of pd_s from 0·1 mm.Hg.cm. to 15 mm.Hg.cm. Typical Paschen curves are given in Fig. 4.6. Paschen's Law follows analytically from the Townsend criterion for breakdown, since α/p and ω are functions of E/p, i.e., of V_s/pd_s. Putting $\alpha/p = f(E/p)$ and $\omega/p = F(E/p)$ in equation 4.7, it follows that

$$1 - \{F(V_s/pd_s)/f(V_s/pd_s)\}\{\exp f(V_s/pd_s) \cdot pd_s - 1\} = 0$$

i.e.,

$$V_s = \psi(pd_s) . \quad . \quad . \quad . \quad . \quad (4.9)$$

which is Paschen's Law.

The general shape of the Paschen curve may be deduced from elementary considerations. At very low pressures the collision frequency is low, so that sufficient ionization is maintained only by increasing the probability of ionization at each collision; consequently the electron velocity, and thus the electric field, must be high (see § 3.1). Hence V_s must increase as p diminishes when p is very low. On the other hand, at the higher pressures the collision frequency is high, and the rate of energy loss correspondingly high, while the energy gained per free path is low unless the field is correspondingly high. Thus $E_s(= V_s/d_s)$ must be increased when p is increased at the high pressures for a given d_s; and the curve must show a minimum V .

The above derivation assumes that the field E is always uniform when pd is changed, but this is the case only when the ratio (L/d) of the linear dimension L of the electrodes to the gap distance d is sufficiently great, the value depending on the gas [167, 202]. At low

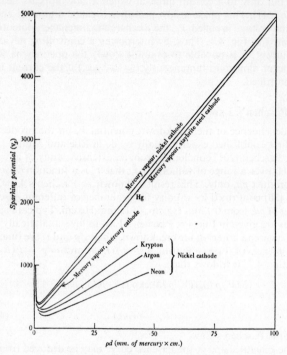

FIG. 4.6. Paschen curves [152]

pressures, especially, charges on the walls of the glass envelope can influence the field in the gap unless the walls are sufficiently remote or are screened.

Observed Paschen curves show that E_s/p diminishes as pd_s increases.

4.8 Cathode Effects

4.8.1 *Theory*. Equation 4.9 shows that in any given gas and for a given value of pd_s the value of V_s depends on (ω/α), which itself can depend on the nature of the cathode when any of the electrode secondary processes γ, δ or ε predominate.

Early measurements by Carr [36] for about fifty different metals could, however, distinguish no important changes in V_s with different electrode materials. This result, appearing to indicate that the cathode surface played no part in the current growth, led Townsend [267] originally to consider that the secondary ionization was mainly due to a process acting entirely in the gas such as the β action. However, no conclusive experimental evidence of the action of this process under these conditions of E/p has so far been obtained, and as a result further work using modern vacuum techniques has been carried out to investigate the role of the cathode surface.

It has been shown above in § 4.5 that the relative efficacy of the various secondary processes β, γ, δ, ε, etc., in any given case cannot easily be found from the shape of the growth of current log I, d curve, since all these processes produce a curve of the same form. However, other characteristics of the processes may be used to distinguish between their action. For example, the β and η processes occur entirely in the gas, and the current growth due to these should be independent of the nature of the cathode surface. With the γ and δ processes, on the other hand, marked dependence of V_s on the nature and work function of the surface is to be expected, as shown in §§ 3.8 and 3.12. Much work has therefore been done to investigate any dependence of V_s, and therefore of ω/α, on the nature of the cathode surface.

The change ΔV_s to be expected in V_s due to a change $\Delta(\omega/\alpha)$ in the secondary coefficient ω/α produced by a change of cathode is given approximately by [153]

$$\Delta V_s = \Delta(\omega/\alpha)/(\omega/\alpha) \cdot f'(E_s/p).$$

The change in V_s due to a change of cathode thus depends on E_s/p, so that ΔV_s is constant when $f'(E_s/p)$ is constant. It is characteristic of discharges in gases that E_s/p changes very little at high gas pressures, and in hydrogen E_s/p falls only from 32 to 28 $V/\text{cm.mm.}$ Hg when pd_s is increased from 90 to 200 mm.Hg.cm. Consequently the Paschen curves for different cathodes having different values of ω/α should be nearly parallel at high pressures; but when V_s is near its minimum value the proportional change $\Delta V_s/V_s$ should be approximately greatest. Thus any influence of the cathode on the sparking potential should be most easily demonstrated in the neighbourhood of the minimum sparking potential V_m. For high values of pd_s the ratio E_s/p is practically constant, so that the proportional change $\Delta V_s/V_s$ is nearly inversely proportional to V_s, and it follows that $\Delta V_s/V_s$ can become small enough to fall within the experimental error.

4.8.2 *Experimental Data*. The sparking potential of hydrogen between parallel-plane electrodes has been measured [153] throughout a range of gas pressures from 1 to 520 mm. Hg for six different de-

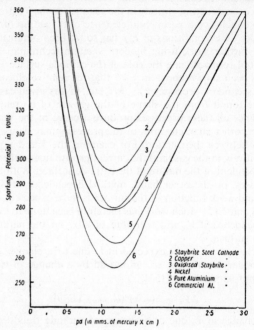

FIG. 4.7. The minimum sparking potential of hydrogen with different cathodes [147]

gassed cathodes: clean and slightly oxidized Staybrite steel, pure and commercial aluminium, nickel and copper, and the values are given in Fig. 4.7. Marked dependence of the sparking potential on the cathode material was found, especially at the minimum values. The change in sparking potential due to a change of cathode at any given pressure was practically constant throughout the pressure range, and at high pressures ($pd_s > 100$) the Paschen curves for hydrogen for the different cathode materials are barely distinguishable. It would follow that, at atmospheric pressure, the material of the cathode would have a negligible effect on the sparking potential of hydrogen even when the secondary ionization processes are entirely cathode-emission processes. In the lower-pressure range ($pd <$ 100 mm.Hg.cm.) the change of the cathode material affects V_s only if the material is clean and de-gassed: otherwise, the surface, having an absorbed gas layer, is practically the same for different cathodes.

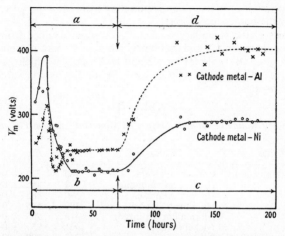

Fig. 4.8. Variation of V_m with time during: (a) cleaning of Al cathode, (b) deposition of Al film on Ni cathode, (c) cleaning of Ni cathode, and (d) deposition of Ni film on Al cathode [150]

A comprehensive investigation of the effect of the state of the cathode has been made [150, 151] by measuring the minimum sparking potential V_m as one metal was gradually deposited on a cathode of different metal. Large changes in V_m were recorded and are shown in Fig. 4.8. With tarnished or oxidized electrodes, it is not easy to obtain accurate values of V_s, the current often becoming intermittent, presumably on account of local changes in the cathode surface. Prolonged heating of the electrodes at 400° C. either *in vacuo* or in hydrogen appeared to be ineffective in removing the last traces of oxide on cathode surfaces; on the other hand, bombardment of the cathode by positive ions of hydrogen (including some photons) had a marked effect on the oxide films in a comparatively short time. When the oxide film had been removed in this way the breakdown

E

potential was easily determined, and regular and reproducible Paschen curves obtained. Typical results are given in Fig. 4.8.

A thin film of an alien metal deposited on a cathode as base altered V_m, but the V_m obtained was characteristic neither of the underlying metal nor of the deposited metal in bulk. In determining the value of V_m (or the cathode emission) characteristic of a pure metal it is desirable to have both electrodes made of the same metal, otherwise the surface of each electrode is liable to become contaminated by deposition of atoms due to sputtering from the other electrode during the outgassing process.

Values of the secondary coefficient ω/α were obtained from the sparking criterion 4.7, and the observed minimum sparking potential V_m are given in Table III for air and hydrogen, for which gas the values of α found by Ayres were used; for air Townsend's values of α were used.

TABLE III

Effect of Nature of Cathode Surface on Minimum Sparking Potential

Gas	Cathode	V_m	E/p	ω/α
Air + Hg vapour.	Copper amalgam	460	720	0·004
	Hg film on aluminium	390	885	0·014
	Hg film on nickel	390	885	0·014
	Hg film on Staybrite steel	390	585	0·006
Air	Aluminium (oxidized)	416	905	0·01
	Nickel (oxidized)	421	957	0·01
Hydrogen (surfaces treated by glow discharge)	Aluminium	243	200	0·04
	Aluminium deposited on nickel	212	200	0·06
	Nickel	289	180	0·02
	Nickel deposited on aluminium	390	245	0·0085
	Staybrite steel	274	190	0·025
	Steel deposited on aluminium	282	190	0·023

It can be seen that great variations in V_m in hydrogen can be produced by changes in the cathode surface. The fact that such changes can be brought about by deposition of thin metallic films indicates the modification of the effective work function of the surface by these films. The deposition of a film of aluminium either on nickel or on Staybrite steel increased the electron emission, while the deposition of a film of nickel on pure aluminium reduced the emission; similarly a film of iron on commercial aluminium reduced the emission. The deposition of thin metallic films on the cathode can be important in measurements in metallic vapours [98, 152] or in mercury-contaminated gases.

4.9 Distinguishing the Secondary Processes

These results demonstrate the predominating influence, at these lower gas pressures, of cathode processes, such as γ or δ, over the purely gas processes, such as β or photo-ionization. The nature of the cathode processes can sometimes be inferred from the form of the variation of the generalized secondary coefficient ω/α with E/p. Secondary emission due to the impact of positive ions on the cathode is mainly a resonance effect (see Chapter III), and depends on the energy released by the ions at the electrode surface, and this energy is made up partly of their potential energy eV_i and partly of their kinetic energy. The change of ionic-kinetic energy $\frac{1}{2}MU^2$ with E/p depends on the nature of the gas; in monatomic gases, for example, this is likely to be small because of charge-transfer effects (see § 3.3), so that in such gases the emission is mainly due to the potential energy of the ions. The potential energy E_i does not depend on E/p, so that in such cases γ should not change greatly other than to show a small increase as E/p increases. The case of photo-electric action, on the other hand, is different. The number of photons emitted in a lamina of gas dx depends on the number of excitations to a given level, and this can be indicated by a term of the form α'/α, where α' is an excitation coefficient of the same general nature as the ionization coefficient α. Thus, the number of photons falling on the cathode, and therefore the electron emission, per ionizing collision in the gas is proportional to α'/α. Now this ratio depends on the shape of the electron-energy distribution function (see Chapter II) and the value of the mean electron energy E_0; in typical cases the ratio α'/α increases as E/p diminishes. Consequently, for electron energies $\sim 4E_0$, an increase in ω/α as E/p diminishes indicates the action of a photo-electric effect. Values of ω/α can be obtained from determinations of the static breakdown potential V_s and the Townsend criterion 4.7, provided α is known accurately for the gas, as well as from measurements of the ionization growth equation 4.3. Examples of the variation of ω/α with E/p are shown in Fig. 4.9 for diatomic gases [20, 147, 150, 151] and for the monatomic gases [136, 137, 284, 285].

With clean, de-gassed cathode surfaces in He or Ne the variation of (ω/α) with E/p is small and generally increases with E/p, thus indicating the predominance of the γ over the δ effect. On the other hand, with un-degassed electrodes or with electrodes having a tarnish layer, an increase of (ω/α) as E/p diminishes is sometimes found at low values of E/p, for example, in air and nitrogen. This result indicates the influence of the δ effect in these conditions when there is reason for believing that the effective work function of the cathode is lower than in the case with clean surfaces. With non-uniform fields

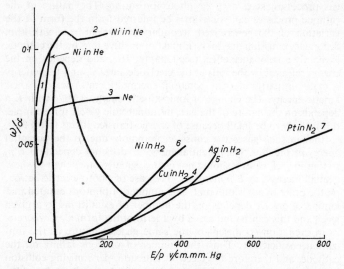

FIG. 4.9. Variation of ω/α with E/p in different gases. Curve 1, [284]; 2, [285]; 3, [136]; 4 and 5, [151]; 6, [147]; 7, [20]

much higher values of the ratio E/p are possible, and the proportion of γ to δ effects may well be different. An interesting technique for distinguishing the various possible cathode secondary processes represented by the coefficients γ, δ, and ε has been used by Hornbeck [116a] and by Molnar [185] in the United States. The technique was similar to that described by Engstrom and Huxford [76], in which the cathode was illuminated not by a steady radiation but by a pulse of ultra-violet light. The resulting ionization pulse produced in argon was recorded oscillographically, from which the time lag of occurrence of its various components after the incidence of the initial pulse could be measured. The latest component, which had a lag ~ 1 m. sec., was considered to be due to the action of metastable atoms. Recent determinations of γ for He$^+$, *in vacuo* made by Hagstrum (see § 3.12.4) with atomically clean surfaces of tungsten and molybdenum, are comparable with those found by Townsend and McCallum ($\sim 0\cdot 1$) from measurements of the growth of ionization currents in helium with a nickel cathode, when back-scattering of electrons near the cathode surface is taken into consideration (see § 2.3). Both in He and Ne Townsend and McCallum found ω/α to be practically independent of E/p over a wide range, and this is consistent with regarding the secondary process as a γ effect in these gases with clean nickel cathodes as indicated above (§ 4.9). Other means of distinguishing between the various possible secondary processes operating in the neighbourhood of the breakdown criterion $V = V_s$ are those based on the dynamical conditions involved in the temporal increase of current when V exceeds V_s by a small amount in the non-steady state. These will be considered below in Chapter VIII.

In concluding this section on the general significance of cathode processes, it is relevant to point out that the lack of consistency which characterizes a large proportion of the published data on the electrical properties of gases is in all probability due to the large differences in the ionization coefficients which can be produced, unless the highest degree of purity of the gases or of cleanliness of the electrode or envelope surfaces is attained. Unless cathode surfaces are atomically clean (i.e., outgassed and free from an oxide or tarnish film), the experimental values of the coefficients γ, δ, or ε found with different tubes or in different laboratories are unlikely to show consistent agreement; they may even differ by orders of magnitude. The coefficient α depends in general upon the gas purity. Owing to the Penning effect, a high degree of purity is necessary with the noble gases, for example; in the diatomic gases, on the other hand, the effects of impurities are not so serious (cf. values of α in various specimens of H_2), especially at the higher values of E/p.

4.10 The V, I Characteristic

Knowledge of the Paschen curve makes it possible to indicate the shape of the V, I characteristic when I increases after V has attained V_s. As the current increases its space charge can become significant. Since the drift velocities of positive ions are $\sim 10^{-2}$ that of electrons, the space charge must be due to the positive ions, and in the steady state becomes greatest at the cathode. A state is finally reached in which a positive layer is set up at distance d_c from the cathode, the voltage between the layer and the cathode being V_c (the cathode fall) corresponding to the value of the product pd_c. When pd exceeds the value corresponding to the minimum sparking potential, an increase of space charge makes the positive layer move nearer to the cathode, thus reducing pd_c. V_c falls accordingly along the Paschen curve, and eventually the space charge will be so near the cathode that pd falls to the value corresponding to the minimum $pd_{min.}$. This last gap ($\sim$ a few free paths) d_c is the cathode dark space. As the current increases further, the space charge spreads laterally if it is possible, maintaining the same distance d_c from the cathode. At this stage an increase in current is obtained without an increase in potential across the cathode fall. The current density is constant and the potential across the gap V_g is independent of I; this condition is called the normal glow discharge. The form of the V, I characteristic is thus as given in Fig. 4.5.

When the discharge has covered the electrodes, further lateral spread is not possible, so that pd must diminish as the current density increases; the voltage then rises, corresponding to the values of $pd < pd_{min.}$ on the Paschen curve. On the other hand, the consideration of § 2.8 shows that if the pressure is high, lateral diffusion is reduced, and an increase of current produces high density which may introduce further ionization processes, such as thermal ionization in the gas, as well as intensified bombardment of the cathode to produce thermionic cathode emission. Thermal effects are unstable —because the ionization increases with the temperature. This latter stage, the transition from the glow to arc, is not so easily established in low-pressure cases as at high pressures, partly because of the lower current density due to the greater lateral diffusion then possible. The cross-section of the current stream I will be largely determined by the lateral diffusion of the electrons as they move across the gap, the diffusion becoming ambi-polar at the higher current densities owing to space charge [243, 244, 280] (see § 2.8.3).

The fact that, after the static breakdown criterion is satisfied ($V = V_s$), the increase of spark current I_D causes a fall in the potential V_D across the gap, led Fuchs [88] to propose the empirical relations between V_D, p, d, and the pre-breakdown current density I

$$V_D = V_s\{1 - \phi(p, d)\sqrt{I}\}$$

and

$$I_D = \psi(p, d)\sqrt{I},$$

where I is the pre-current density passing before the breakdown is produced.

It has been suggested [66] that

$$V_s - V_D = KI_D{}^2$$

where K is constant, but it has been found experimentally that

$$V_s - V_D = KI_D$$

Explanations have been attempted on the basis of the variation of α and ω/α with E. Irradiation of the cathode by an external source can also affect the value of V_s, and the fall can be appreciable with $I_0 \sim 10^{-8}$ A./cm.². It is found experimentally that

$$V_{s(0)} - V_{s(r)} = G\sqrt{I_0}$$

where $V_{s(0)}$ and $V_{s(r)}$ are the potentials with and without radiation and G a constant.

4.11 The Similarity Principle

Before concluding this chapter it is pertinent to discuss the similarity principle, although this principle is not limited to the case of uniform fields or even to breakdown. The principle has considerable use in comparing breakdown relationships under different conditions, as well as providing information concerning elementary processes. The following is a brief account of the nature and application of the similarity principle to electrical discharges.

4.11.1 *Similarity Relationships.* Consider two geometrically similar discharge systems 1 and 2, such as two tubes containing parallel-plate electrodes in which a leading dimension d (e.g., gap separation) in 2 is k times greater than d in 1. The potential V_1 at any given point P_1 in the gap due to the surface charge is given by

$$V_1 = \int \sigma_1 dS_1/r_1$$

where dS_1 is an elementary surface area of charge surface density σ_1 on the electrodes over which the integral is taken, and r_1 is the radial distance between P_1 and dS_1. At a corresponding point P_2 in system II the potential is

$$\begin{aligned}
V_2 &= \int \sigma_2 dS_2/r_2 \\
&= \int k^2 \sigma_2 dS_1/kr_1, \text{ since } \begin{cases} dS_2 = k^2 dS_1, \\ r_2 = kr_1, \end{cases} \\
&= V_1
\end{aligned}$$

when

$$\sigma_2 = \sigma_1/k$$

It follows that

$$E_2 = E_1/k$$

and if the gas pressures are arranged so that

$$p_2 = p_1/k$$

then

$$E_1/p_1 = E_2/p_2$$

and

$$p_1 d_1 = p_2 d_2$$

Hence all quantities, which are functions only of E/p, are the same in the two systems. From Chapter II it can be seen that examples of such quantities are electron- and ion-drift velocities, and electron mean energies; and in § 4.3 it has been shown that α/p and ω/α are also functions of E/p, and it further follows that other quantities derived from these are also functions of E/p, and will thus be the same in the two systems. For instance,

$$\int \alpha ds = \int f(E/p) p \,.\, ds$$

but pds must be the same in 1 and 2, so that $\int \alpha ds$ is the same. Thus if there are initiatory currents of equal magnitudes and distributions in the two systems,

$$V_1 = V_2$$

and

$$I_1 = I_2$$

Thus the V, I characteristics of the two systems are the same. Since V_s is the value of V for a small self-maintained current, it follows that V_s is the same when pd is constant, which is Paschen's Law. It follows readily that the current densities J in the two similar systems are related

$$J_1 = I_1/dS_1 = k^2 I_2/dS_2 = k^2 J_2 = (p_1/p_2)^2 J_2$$

so that

$$J/p^2 = \text{const.}$$

Space charge densities ρ are related by

$$\rho_1 = \partial^2 V_1/\partial x_1^2 = k^2 \partial^2 V_2/\partial x_2^2$$
$$= k^2 \rho_2$$

Thus space charges will not invalidate the relation $V_1 = V_2$.

Transformation ratios for various parameters in similar systems are given in Table IV.

TABLE IV

Similarity Transformations for Discharge Parameters

System	1	2
Linear dimension	a	ka
Gas density or pressure.	p	p/k
Potential across gap	V	V
Field strength	E	E/k
Surface charge density	σ	σ/k
Space charge density	ρ	ρ/k^2
Total mass of gas between plates . . .	M	Mk^2
Total electric charge in gas	e	ek
Ratio of density of ionized to neutral molecules	n_i/n_n	n_i/n_nk
Electric current	I	I
Current density	J	J/k^2
Voltage current characteristic. . . .	V, I	V, I
Temporal growth rate of current . . .	$\partial I/\partial t$	$\partial I/k\partial t$

In considering similarity for high-frequency fields the parameter is no longer E/p only, but involves also a time factor which must be changed by the factor k. This parameter must contain a term f/p (f is the frequency of the field) as well as E/p (see Chapter IX).

4.11.2 *Physical Significance of Similarity Principle*. The similarity principle is a consequence of the nature of the significant fundamental gas processes. In similar systems $E/p = $ constant, so that any process which occurs at a rate dependent only upon E/p conforms with the similarity principle. Thus, collision processes which are significant in similar systems are those dependent only upon E/p, and the general nature of such processes can sometimes be found from application of the similarity principle.

The mean energy ($\frac{1}{2}mu^2$) of a cloud of electrons in a gas is dependent upon E/p only (see § 2.7); therefore, the velocity of agitation u is a function of E/p. The electron drift velocity is $2Eel/3mu$, and is also a function of E/p. The drift velocity of positive ions is EeL/MU, where U is the mean thermal velocity, and also is a function of E/p.

The probabilities of ionization and excitation are functions of the energy of the colliding electrons, and are functions of E/p. The diffusion coefficient of electrons is $\frac{1}{3}lu$ and is $(1/p) \cdot f(E/p)$.

In considering the stability of a discharge it is sufficient to show that concentrations of charged particles in space, and at the boundaries, remain constant when carrier production and destruction balance.

4.11.3 *Physical Considerations*. The time factor introduces another consideration. In two similar gap systems the drift velocities of corresponding electron avalanches are the same, so that the avalanches do not reach corresponding planes in the two systems in the same time. The time element for the larger system is correspondingly larger when

$$(\Delta t)_2 = k \cdot (\Delta t)_1$$

Consequently, for the rates of increase of current, say, in 1 and 2, it follows that at corresponding times

$$(\partial I/\partial t)_2 = (\partial I/\partial t)_1 \cdot 1/k$$

In other words, the rate of increase of electron density in the two systems at corresponding times obeys the relation

$$(\partial \rho/\partial t)_2 = (\partial \rho/\partial t)_1 \cdot 1/k^3$$

That is, the rate of increase of ρ transforms from one system to the similar system k times larger in the ratio $1 : k^3$. This is a very important relation. Only if a process of generation or of destruction in the body of the gas transforms according to this relation will such a process occur to any significant extent in systems which obey the similarity relation.

Similarly at the boundaries, the wall-current density J_1, for instance, transforms as $1 : k^2$; so that only if a transport process at the boundaries (glass walls or the electrodes) is compatible with this will that process be of importance in discharges which obey the similarity relation. Breakdown criteria relate to particular discharges with which I is small and V high; hence the above considerations apply to breakdown characteristics.

Consideration of the various processes of ionization by collision, diffusion, drift, recombination, and attachment, based on the analysis of Chapter II, may thus be used to find which of these gas processes will or will not disturb similarity. Examples of the application of the similarity principle will be found in later chapters.

4.11.4 *Application of the Similarity Principle*. Important cases of ionization are those involving metastable atoms in gas mixtures, and the processes in which they take part have been discussed above in § 3.4. It is interesting to consider whether processes involving metastable atoms conform to the similarity principle.

In a pure gas metastable atoms are formed by single electron impact, and this process transforms as the α process, and therefore obeys the similarity relation. In equilibrium the production of metastables will balance destruction, and the two processes must therefore conform to similarity. In a pure gas destruction takes place mainly at the walls of the tube, to which there is lateral loss by diffusion, or by atom collisions. Metastable atoms may also be destroyed in the gas by electron or atom collision processes. With sufficient impurity, metastable atoms will eventually ionize in collisions of the second kind, and this means that for every metastable atom produced an electron is also produced. This is equivalent to ionization with an effective ionization potential of $V_{met.}$, and the Penning effect will then transform as a similarity relationship. Thus, in a pure gas the processes of generation and destruction of metastable atoms transform similarly, and in fact, this has been established experimentally. Also, when there is a dominant process of destruction of metastables due to the Penning effect, this process also will transform. In the intermediate stage, when only a trace of impurity, possibly too small to detect, is present, three distinct processes can occur: viz., diffusion to the walls, collisions with electrons, and collisions with impure molecules; but these separate terms are of different dimensions and do not transform by the same factor. There is some evidence for these effects [299]. For example, when helium was purified continually, in the later stages the similarity relation in a co-axial system was upset but finally re-established for the purest gas specimen.

Considerations of similarity have been applied in low-pressure discharges in air, hydrogen, and helium both for breakdown and for maintained discharges with high frequency as well as with static fields, and these will be discussed below (Chapters VII and IX). It has been shown experimentally that another process which does not conform to the similarity relations is the emission of electrons from electrodes under the action of electric fields $> 10^4$ V/cm., as has been observed in tarnished surfaces. This accounts for the fact that breakdown in gases at very high pressures when such values of electric field obtain does not obey Paschen's Law, as described in Chapter VI.

A formal treatment of the collision processes can be made based on the equations of continuity and boundary conditions for each type of particle. For example, in the case of a gas 1 containing traces of an impurity of a gas 2 the density $n_1{}^m$ of metastable atoms of 1 must satisfy

$$\frac{\partial n_1{}^m}{\partial t} + \frac{\partial i_1{}^m}{\partial x} = \frac{\partial n_1{}^m}{\partial t} - \left\{ D_1{}^m \frac{\partial^2 n_1{}^m}{\partial x^2} - \frac{\partial}{\partial x}(v_1 n_1{}^m) \right\}$$

where $n_1{}^m$ is the concentration of metastables in gas 1, $i_1{}^m$ the current flow of metastables, and v_1 the compensating flow of the gas as a whole in the tube.

The net rate of generation of metastables, which must equal the above expression, is also

$$= \alpha n_1{}^n n_e \underset{\text{(Penning effect)}}{\quad - \quad} \alpha_2 n_2{}^n n_1{}^m \underset{\substack{\text{(Step-wise ionization} \\ \text{and excitation)}}}{\quad - \quad} (\alpha_3 + \alpha_4) n_1{}^m n_e$$

$$\underset{\substack{\text{(Destruction of } n_1{}^m \text{ by} \\ \text{collisions with } n_1{}^n)}}{- \; \alpha_5 n_1{}^n n_1{}^m} \quad + \quad \underset{\substack{\text{(Excited atoms falling back} \\ \text{to metastable levels in the gas)}}}{b n_1{}^{ex}}$$

where the α's and b are self-explanatory collisional coefficients, and n_e is electron concentration. Each side of the equation integrates to

$$\underset{\substack{\text{(Metastables produced} \\ \text{by neutralization of ions} \\ \text{at wall and cathode)}}}{- \; Fi_{1+}(0)} \quad + \quad \underset{\substack{\text{(Metastables} \\ \text{changed to} \\ \text{ground state} \\ \text{at cathode)}}}{G n_1{}^m(0)} \quad + \quad \frac{d}{dt} \int n_1{}^m dx$$

The importance of any of the above collision processes (e.g., step-wise ionization $\alpha_4 n_1{}^m n_e$) can be assessed for any given set of conditions by considering whether they predict similarity, and whether it is found. In that way information may be obtained about the nature of the processes either of ionization or of destruction of metastable or excited atoms.

CHAPTER V

Breakdown at the Higher Gas Pressures
$(150 < pd < 1,000$ mm.Hg.cm.$)$

5.1 The Problem

In the early work on the spatial growth of ionization which led to the Townsend theory the sources of steady potential for the gap were usually storage batteries. There was therefore no problem of voltage instability, and the ratio E/p could be easily maintained sufficiently constant, as was necessary in such work. The investigations were mostly carried out at the lower pressures when the parameter $pd \lesssim 150$ mm.Hg.cm., and because of the absence of evidence to the contrary, it was assumed as probable that the same mechanism of ionization growth set the breakdown criterion also at higher pressures, the original theory being generalized to take into account later knowledge of atomic-collision phenomena. Of particular interest, because of its practical importance, was the case of the 1-cm. spark in the atmosphere; but it was only after the introduction of methods of providing high potentials from impulse generators and of oscillographic recording techniques that breakdown at high pressure was systematically investigated.

In 1926 Rogowski [222, 247], at Aachen, applied a sharply peaked impulse of e.m.f. to a gap in air and found that the voltage collapsed in times $\lesssim 10^{-6}$ sec. or 10^{-7} sec. This result appeared to introduce a considerable difficulty in the explanation of the spark on the Townsend theory of static breakdown, because the action of a secondary process involving the motion of positive ions to the cathode, for instance, should require times at least 10^2 larger than those observed, due to the long transit time $(d/W_+ \sim 10^{-5}$ sec.$)$ of the ions across a 1-cm. gap. It was inferred from this result that positive ions could not have crossed the gap in the time available, and this was further taken to indicate that no secondary process at all took part in the build up to the spark, because at the time little consideration was given to the faster photo-electric secondary process δ. It was considered that the Townsend mechanism required several successive avalanches, *even with over-volted gaps*, and was therefore a comparatively slow mechanism. At that time, however, no rigorous theoretical investigation of the temporal growth of ionization due to primary and generalized secondary (α and ω/α) processes had been made for fields $E > V_s/d$, i.e., for the non-steady state. Thus the true significance of the observed formative time of spark breakdown with an over-volted gap could not then have been assessed.

Now this conclusion that secondary processes did not occur in the pre-breakdown current could readily be tested by measuring the growth of photo-electric currents in the gas under a *static* electric field, and examining the shape of the log I, d curve obtained, in exactly the same way as had been done at the lower gas pressures (see § 4.3). The action of secondary processes must give a curve in accordance with the relation

$$I = I_0 \exp\alpha d/\{1 - (\omega/\alpha)(\exp \alpha d - 1)\} \quad . \quad . \quad (5.1)$$

while the action of only an α process (with $\omega/\alpha = 0$) would give a graph following the equation

$$I = I_0 \exp \alpha d$$

and thus give a straight line for the log I, d graph. Experimental investigations on these lines were carried out by Masch [170], Paavola [199], Sanders [227], Posin [206], and by Hochberg and Sandberg [114]. Typical [164] log I, d graphs obtained in air were apparently linear up to the value of d at which a breakdown flash occurred. When an upcurving of the log I, d graph was present the cause of this breakdown was readily explained because of the action of any or all of the secondary processes represented by the coefficient ω/α. On the other hand, with linear growth curves which indicated nothing but the action of an α process, breakdown at these higher values of pd apparently presented a problem. If this view (that no secondary processes occurred in the uniform field at high pressures) was correct, clearly some other mechanism must have acted extremely rapidly in distance just when d approached d_s (or V approached V_s).

5.2 *Kanal* and Streamer Theories

The interpretation of the experimental data in static uniform fields (that the spark-breakdown criterion can be set at these high values of the parameter without the influence of any ω/α process) was one of the main factors which led finally to the proposal by Loeb of a streamer theory of the breakdown criterion in place of the Townsend mechanism: the comparatively narrow luminous tracks occurring at spark breakdown at these higher pressures were called streamers. Ingenious attempts had, however, been made by Loeb [162, 163], by Rogowski [221] and by Frank and von Hippel [112] suitably to modify the Townsend theory for conditions at high pressure. Interesting photographs of the propagation of spark tracks in air containing alcohol and water vapours have been obtained by Raether using a cloud-chamber technique and overvoltages ~ 10–20 per cent of V_s. The rates of *propagation of luminosity* [165] in these tracks were measured and found to be $\gtrsim 10^7$ cm./sec. Consideration of these photographs led Raether to propose a *kanal* theory of spark breakdown dependent on the space charge produced in tracks such as these. On both these theories it was considered originally that the Townsend criterion

$$1 - (\omega/\alpha)(\exp \alpha d - 1) = 0 . \quad . \quad . \quad . \quad (5.2)$$

did not apply to static breakdown when $pd \sim 760$ mm.Hg.cm. which corresponded to a 1-cm. gap in the atmosphere. It was thought that the mechanism of current growth based on the continuous development of ionization by primary and secondary processes in undistorted fields would be too slow to account for the observed high rates of propagation of luminosity. This question will be discussed in more detail in Chapter VIII.

On both *kanal* and streamer theories additional electrons are considered to be generated in the gap by photo-ionization by photons produced in the primary electron avalanche, but this ionization becomes very rapid only when the original field becomes highly distorted by a positive ion space charge at the head of the avalanche. The new electrons are assumed to initiate additional avalanches near the head of the main avalanche, producing rapid effective propagation of the avalanche across the gap, which, in effect, is bridged. It was maintained that transit times $\gtrsim 10^{-7}$ sec. are feasible. Other considerations were also raised. No definite evidence had been found to indicate any influence of the cathode on breakdown potentials at high gas pressures, and this had been taken to indicate that under these conditions γ and δ effects are negligible [165]. However, it has been shown above in § 4.8 that normal changes in the magnitudes of the usual cathode mechanisms would in any case produce negligible changes in V_s at the high gas pressures, so that absence of measurable changes in V_s does not necessarily imply absence of cathode processes. Again, it was considered that the comparatively narrow spark track found at high pressures, rather than the more diffuse glow obtained at low pressures, indicated a different ionization mechanism. It might be noted, however, that at high pressures the lateral diffusion of the avalanche is naturally reduced (Chapter II) and a wide diffuse track not easily obtained.

Both these forms of streamer theory are qualitative, and a quantitative theory of the breakdown criterion relating the sparking potential under static fields to ionization coefficients (for ions and photons) which can be measured in any given gas has not yet been given. However, both aspects were based on the following assumptions. It was assumed that the secondary processes β, γ, δ, ε, etc., do not contribute to the pre-breakdown growth, but that when the field produced by the space charge at the avalanche head suddenly attains a magnitude such that α is enhanced and photo-ionization becomes significant, a sharp increase of current is produced. Thus, in a static field the log I, d pre-breakdown curves should be linear. The process of the generation of the requisite photons, and the way in which such photons produce the extra ionization and contribute to the increase in current, were not quantitatively explained. These theories are applied to air, and it is not easy to see how the mechanism dependent only on photo-ionization can occur in pure gases, and especially in monatomic gases. Nevertheless, the streamer theories were originally considered [165, 212] as accounting, in a general qualitative way, for available data in the range $150 < pd < 1,000$ mm.Hg.cm. However, a satisfactory theory of breakdown must express the breakdown potential V_s in terms of measurable coefficients or other properties, and two criteria on the *kanal* and streamer theories have been proposed.

5.2.1 *Raether's Criterion* [133, 215, 132]. The initial Townsend avalanche sets up positive space charge at its head which distorts the original applied field there. The space charge is dependent on the number of ions in the avalanche, and Raether, from cloud-chamber studies with gaps over-volted at various percentages up to 20 per cent, suggested that when the ion population exceeds a certain quantity N, the distortion of the field is sufficient to produce a more rapid transit velocity, together with a rapidly increasing ionization, by which the avalanche builds up into first an anode-directed *kanal*, and later a cathode-directed *kanal* which bridges the gap. Raether's criterion can thus be expressed as a critical amplification:

$$\exp \alpha d = N_1 = \text{constant} \quad . \quad . \quad . \quad (5.3)$$

and by suitable empirical choice of N, using known values of α, it is possible to calculate values of d_s which are approximately the same as those observed in the static case. The critical value of αd has been given as about 18 to 20.

5.2.2 *Meek's Criterion*. Meek [177, 178] proposed a breakdown criterion for Loeb's streamer idea based on somewhat different considerations. The space-charge field at the head of the avalanche was assumed strong enough to attract photo-electrons produced by the rapid absorption of photons in the vicinity of the avalanche head. These were considered to initiate small avalanches moving from all directions radially to the avalanche head, extending the positive charge and completely ionizing the gap. To find a criterion it was then postulated that conduction, i.e., complete breakdown, will occur by processes which become important when the space-charge field is of the same order as the applied field. As with Raether's *kanal*, this condition will occur approximately within the time necessary for the avalanche to build up the requisite space charge, because the succeeding processes are postulated to be fast. An approximate calculation can be made of the order of the field produced by a spherical space charge, and Meek related this to the value of the previously undistorted field E by a constant of proportionality K, and found the empirical relation for air, assuming $K = 1$,

$$\alpha d + \log \alpha/p = 14\cdot46 + \log E/p - \tfrac{1}{2}\log pd + \log d \quad (5.4)$$

This is the Meek spark criterion. When α/p, d, p, and V_s are known, it is possible to find K; and the equation was considered then able to give V_s for other values of pd. Values deduced in this way were very approximately the same as those previously published at high pd, a region, incidentally, for which there is a dearth of reliable data.

5.2.3 *Comments*. These criteria do not take into consideration quantitatively the actual physical mechanism of ionization development or even the processes postulated as essential for breakdown, such as the production of photons and the way they contribute to the current. In analysing the derivation of Meek's equation, Zeleny [303] pointed out that the space-charge field would not act in the way proposed; further, suitable values of the important factor K had to be assumed. The equation is in fact empirical, giving values of V_s which differ very little from those deduced by the simple expression $\exp \alpha d = \text{constant}$. Fisher [77] also drew attention to the inconsistencies in conclusions drawn from this criterion. Both the Raether and Meek criteria thus, in effect, reduce to the same analytic form which, incidentally, is formally similar to the Townsend criterion for static breakdown. At high values of pd, V_s does not vary greatly with (ω/α), and for calculating V_s the Townsend criterion for static

F

breakdown can be, as Schumann [245] suggested, approximately expressed as

$$\exp \alpha d = \text{constant} \quad . \quad . \quad . \quad . \quad (5.5)$$

Thus all three criteria appear very similar.

It may also be pointed out here that for the testing of these criteria proposed for the setting of the breakdown potentials V_s for various gases, accurate data in α/p, pd, and V_s are required, especially when $pd \gtrsim 1,000$ mm.Hg.cm. for stable or controlled conditions of the electrode surfaces in uniform fields. Application of these streamer concepts to the explanation of the filamentary nature of the spark track must await a more quantitative treatment than is now possible with the concepts in their present state. This is particularly the case in regard to the suggested rapid ionization development by the α process, together with photo-ionization in the distorted field stated to exist at the head of the avalanche. At present, the terms *kanal* or streamer mechanisms are applied to the *assumed* rapid mechanism of ionization development, without knowing precisely what that mechanism is. On general grounds, it is not easy to see why the avalanche should be narrow, if it is being generated by subsidiary avalanches fed in radially from all sides (see § 5.4 below).

However, both *kanal* and streamer concepts, when applied to breakdown in static uniform fields, lead to criteria controlled by sudden space-charge distortion and a growth of pre-breakdown ionization which should give a linear log I, d graph up to the distance d_s at which the criterion for breakdown is set. Consequently, it now becomes important to examine those particular published data on the growth of currents which had been taken as showing that no secondary ionization occurred at high values of pd, in order to find whether, if a secondary process did in fact occur, those particular measurements could have disclosed them.

5.3 Experimental Work on Spatial Growth

Analysis of those data showed that neither the range nor the accuracy of those experimental investigations were sufficient to indicate the action of any secondary process if it had existed; the stability of the electric fields used (rectified and smoothed A.C.) was not sufficiently great to maintain adequate constancy in E/p. If E/p fluctuated during the measurements of I, the breakdown could occur when at the peak of a ripple in E, for a smaller value of d than that to be expected on the assumed value of E/p. Calculation shows that if the growth of photo-electric currents in air is to be measured in the region where $E/p \sim 41\cdot6$ V/cm.mm.Hg., then distances and gap voltages must be measured with high accuracy: measurement of I in the range 10^{-14}–10^{-9} A. at high values of pd requires the use of

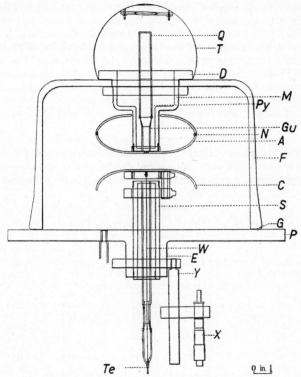

FIG. 5.1. Ionization chamber [157]

high potentials steady to within 0·1 per cent [157, 158], and work in this field using dry, mercury-free gases will now be described.

5.3.1 *Later Work on Ionization Growth.* An ionization chamber (Fig. 5.1) capable of operating at 100 kV with potential steady to within 0·1 per cent with electrode separations up to 5 cm. was designed and used at Swansea to measure the growth of small initial photo-electric currents I_0 ($\sim 10^{-14}$ amp.) in air over a range of E/p from 39 to 45 V/cm.mm.Hg. at a pressure of 200 mm.Hg., for values of pd up to about 760 mm.Hg.cm., thus including the value of that parameter corresponding to a 1-cm. spark in the atmosphere.

Apart from the experimental difficulties connected with the maintenance of the stability at high voltages, there were certain operating difficulties due to the use of air. Air can produce progressive changes in the cathode surface due to the formation of oxides and other tarnish layers. Such layers can have a profound effect upon the electron emissive properties of the surface due to the action of positive ions near the surface in the presence of the electric field [159, 154, 189]. Thus, the maintenance of even a small ionization current in air can not only change the photo-electric sensitivity of the cathode, but also change the secondary emission under positive-ion bombardment. Care has therefore to be taken in the treatment of the surface and the measurement of the current.

It is important, however, to investigate the electrical properties and the breakdown criterion of air because considerable previous work has been done with that gas and also because of its technological importance. A typical set of results obtained in the investigation

TABLE V

Experimental Values [158] *of* I_0, α/p, (ω/α) *and Calculated Values o, d_s in air for Various Values of* E/p *when* $p = 200$ *mm.Hg.*

E/p (V/cm./mm. Hg)	$10^{15} I_0$ (A)	α/p (cm. mm. Hg)$^{-1}$	$10^6 (\omega/\alpha)$	d_s (cm.)
39	1	0·0161	8	3·73
40	6	0·0181	23	2·94
40	20	0·0181	$\geqslant 150$	—
41	6	0·0196	40	2·53
42	6	0·0224	46	2·22
43	5	0·0252	113	1·83
44	3	0·0295	105	1·57
45	6	0·0345	84	1·37

at Swansea [158, 157] is given in Fig. 5.2 as graphs of log I, d. The curves show that for distances up to about 1·25 cm. the relation between log I and d was linear for all values of E/p from 39 to 45, which includes the case corresponding to a cm. gap in the atmosphere. For larger values of d the curves departed from linearity, giving measurable values of ω/α, and showing the existence of secondary processes. Values of α were obtained from the slope of the linear portions and values of ω/α from the upcurving sections, and these are given in Table V as functions of E/p. Observations were made as close as

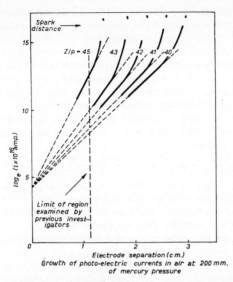

FIG. 5.2. Growth of photoelectric currents in dry, mercury-free air [158]

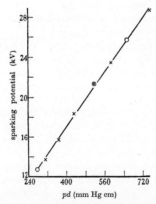

FIG. 5.3. Calculated ($\times$) and observed (O) sparking potentials in dry, mercury-free air [157]

85

possible to the sparking distance, but in no case was a spark obtained *before* the curve indicated the presence of an ω/α process. These values of ω/α and α when substituted in equation 5.2 give the theoretical value of V_s. After each set of current-growth measurements a single but careful measurement of V_s was made, and these are given in Fig. 5.3, which shows agreement in the range 10–30 kV between theoretical and measured values. Fig. 5.3 calculated (x) and observed (o) sparking potentials in air [157].

5.3.2 *The Mechanism Setting the Breakdown Criterion in Air in Uniform Static Fields.* The above results are consistent with the following conclusions.

Even at high pd (spark in air) equation 5.1 still describes the growth of ionization currents in uniform fields, involving primary and secondary processes similar to the case of low pd. The mechanism which produces the breakdown criterion is thus that which also provides the growth of ionization in the pre-breakdown regime, from which it is a continuous development.

No evidence was obtained for the sudden appearance of any new mechanism setting the spark criterion when $d = d_s$. Since the values of α and ω/α which satisfy the breakdown criterion were those obtained from the growth of a small current at values of $d < d_s$, it would appear that the space charge of the current in the vicinity of $d = d_s$ had not developed to alter α and ω/α significantly. The secondary ionization observed was consistent with cathode emission due to incidence of ions and photons.

In agreement with these conclusions, Kohrmann and Raether also consider from their later work that, when αd is less than about 18, the electron avalanche develops in terms of primary α and secondary processes in a negligible space-charge field and in times $\sim$ several gap transit times. However, they consider that when $\alpha d \geqslant 18$, the field distortion due to space charge will have a controlling influence, and the development will become extremely rapid. For the 1-cm. gap in the atmosphere, and with static fields Raether and Kohrmann [133] have found that $\alpha d_s < 18$, so that on their view also the breakdown criterion should be set by the Townsend criterion 5.1, as indeed is found experimentally.

5.3.3 *Experimental Data on Growth in Nitrogen and Hydrogen.* The use of nitrogen avoided difficulties which resulted from the progressive oxidation of the cathode. A careful investigation of the photo-electric efficiency of the cathode was made [68], and after treatment in a glow discharge in nitrogen the photo-electric yield was constant. The use of nitrogen, however, involved further experimental difficulties because of the necessity for increasing the sensitivity of the current-measuring apparatus compared with that required for air. The anode voltages (10–40 kV) were stabilized to 0·05 per cent, and the growth of currents was measured using initial photoelectric currents of 6×10^{-15} to 6×10^{-11} A. from an area 0·3 cm.[2]

Consideration of the case of nitrogen was necessary in order to find whether: (1) an upcurving of the log I, d graph occurred in nitrogen as well as in air, in order to see whether breakdown in air (a mixture) is fundamentally different from that in a single gas because of the possibility of photo-ionization; (2) the breakdown potential and secondary coefficients depended on the current density, i.e., whether double-ionization processes or photon production by recombination processes occurred; and (3) space charge was significant in setting a breakdown criterion.

Typical results for nitrogen are given in Fig. 5.4. These show that nitrogen also gives an upcurving in the log I, d graphs as did air. Fig. 5.5 shows the curves obtained at the same E/p up to the breakdown distance d_s for three different initial currents. Within the experimental error, these curves have the same slope, indicating the same value of α, and the same value of d_s or V_s, and thus the same value of (ω/α). This showed that the primary and secondary ionization did not depend upon the current, since the coefficients were the same over a wide range of current density; production of photons by recombination processes depending on the square of the current did not take place to any great extent. Further, no significant effects attributable to space charges occurred in setting the conditions for V_s. Calculations by Crowe, Bragg, and Thomas [52] of space-charge effects for this range of currents are in agreement with this conclusion. When the points of the three curves of Fig. 5.5 are plotted as log I/I_0, d, they all fall on the same curve. Previous measurements of Posin giving different curves for different currents had been taken to indicate the effects of space charge in the gas ([164], p. 386); but such variations with current are to be expected unless the cathode surface is treated to give it stable properties.

After careful treatment of the electrode surfaces by glow discharges in hydrogen, growth curves [49, 50, 51] were measured in that gas, and typical curves are given in Fig. 5.6. Similar growth curves have also been given for untreated aluminium cathodes by Wilkes, Hopwood and Peacock [298]. Comparison of Figs. 5.3, 5.4, and 5.6, giving growths in air, nitrogen, and hydrogen at high pressure, with Fig. 4.3, relating to these gases at low pressures shows that the growth curves are of the same form.

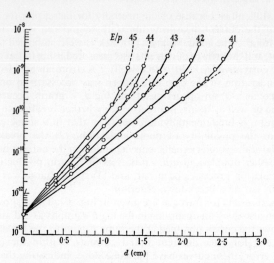

FIG. 5.4. Log I, d curves for nitrogen at values of E/p from 41 to 45 V/cm.mm.Hg at a pressure of 300 mm.Hg [68]

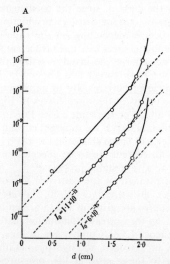

FIG. 5.5. Log I, d graphs obtained over a large range of initial current I_0 from an area 0·3cm.[2] [68]

5.3.4 *Conclusions.* The above experimental data support the view that the generalized mechanism of ionization growth based on the continuous development of ionization by primary and secondary processes is applicable over the wide range of conditions in different gases which has so far been quantitatively examined, i.e., at least up

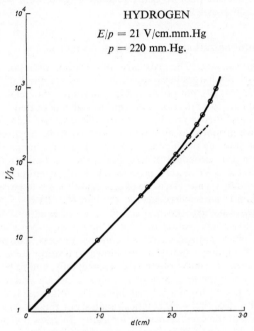

FIG. 5.6. Log I/I_0, d for H_2 at low E/p

to $pd = 1,000$ mm.Hg.cm. and including the case of a 1-cm. gap in the atmosphere. The results also show that the criterion for breakdown in static uniform fields is set *before* space charge significantly alters the ionization coefficients, which are then determined by the applied field. Further, in this mechanism the development of the avalanches is mainly maintained from behind by a secondary ionization process which is the more effective the nearer to the cathode it acts, and most efficient when it acts at the cathode itself. It would appear, also, that the relative importance of the various possible secondary processes is influenced (in uniform field gaps) by the nature and geometry of the cathode. Thus, the streamer and *kanal* concept of a breakdown criterion set by the field distortion due to the avalanche space charge is not in accordance with the experimental data for uniform field static breakdown. Before discussing other aspects it is of interest to consider photo-ionization as a secondary mechanism, the requisite photons being generated by collision processes in the electron avalanche.

5.4 Photo-ionization in the Electron Avalanche

5.4.1 *Introduction.* The existence of ionizing radiations emitted from spark discharges has been known for more than half a century [261, 262, 264, 69], but little reliable quantitative data existed. In recent years photo-ionization has been strongly advocated by Raether for his *kanal* theory and by Loeb for the streamer view, albeit on qualitative grounds, as an essential process in the electrical breakdown of gases at the higher pressures. The importance of photo-ionization as a secondary process lies in the fact that it is a process similar to the positive ion β process, taking place entirely in the gas, not depending on any electrode effects, and thought to have obvious application in a discharge such as the lightning flash.

In view of the experimental confirmation of equation (5.1), however, at these high values of *pd* it is now necessary to investigate whether photo-ionization, as a secondary process, can produce a growth of the important pre-breakdown ionization currents in accordance with the curve observed experimentally, and so be included in the group of possible secondary processes which satisfy equation 5.2, the criterion for spark breakdown. The following is a brief account of a quantitative theoretical analysis of the action of photo-ionization in the development of ionization in gases under uniform electric fields. Fig. 5.7 shows a plane-parallel gap *d* in a gas; *E* is the applied field. I_0 electrons leave the cathode per second, and produce an avalanche. Suppose that photons with sufficiently high energy are produced as a result of excitation in the avalanche. These will travel in all directions: some will be absorbed by the gas atoms, producing ionization and excitation. Of the atoms excited, a fraction will fluoresce and re-emit photons of the same wavelength. These can be given off in any direction, and so will cause a redistribution of the radiation intensity. The rest of the excited atoms will degenerate by returning to states other than the ground state, emitting photons of longer wavelengths which will not be capable of ionizing other gas atoms. The new electrons produced by the ionizing absorptions will give rise to subsidiary electron avalanches which will contribute to the total current I.

The problems are, first, to find whether the processes can lead to a criterion on the lines of equation 5.2, from which the sparking distance or sparking potential can be predicted; and secondly, to find whether these processes can lead to growth of the initial current I_0 in accordance with the experimental relation 5.1.

In doing this, it is necessary first to consider whether the essential

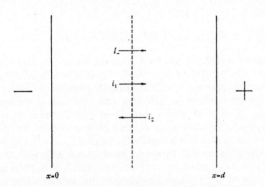

Fig. 5.7. The electron current and light intensities at a distance x from the cathode of a plane parallel gap [69]

high-energy photons can in fact be produced. In pure gases photons with energies sufficient to produce ionization could be produced by the excitation of an ion or by recombination of an ion and electrons. These processes, involving both ions and electrons, will consequently depend on the square of the current. If they were the predominant processes causing breakdown in pure gases, a marked dependence of I on the value of I_0 would then be observed. That no such dependence was detected in nitrogen shows that in simple gases the requisite photons are not produced and that photo-ionization plays no significant role in pure gases. In air, a mixture of gases, on the other hand, photo-ionization can take place. Electrons can excite a nitrogen molecule to levels ~ 15 eV, and the high-energy photons produced can subsequently ionize an oxygen molecule, which has an ionization potential lower than 15 eV. The process, not being dependent on the square of the current, would conform to the observations on the growth of currents. There is also recent experimental evidence that such a process does occur in air (see § 3.5). Thus, air is a gas in which photo-ionization can occur, and it is necessary to investigate whether the process is important in the breakdown mechanism in uniform fields in air.

5.4.2 *Solution of the Continuity Equations.* The theoretical treatment of the growth of ionization involves a solution of the following continuity equations.

$$\left.\begin{array}{l} \partial L_-/\partial x = \alpha\, L_- + \mu_i(i_1 + i_2) \\[1mm] \dfrac{\partial i_1}{\partial x} = (\theta/2)L_- - \mu_i i_1 - \mu_e i_1 + (\mu_r/2)(i_1 + i_2) \\[1mm] -\dfrac{\partial i_2}{\partial x} = (\theta/2)L_- - \mu_i i_2 - \mu_e i_2 + (\mu_r/2)(i_1 + i_2) \end{array}\right\} \quad . \quad (5.6)$$

These relate the electron current L_- with the photon currents in either direction i_1 and i_2, at the plane x with the various ionization and absorption cross-sections. θ is the number of photons produced on the average by an electron in travelling unit distance along the field. $N\mu_i$ is the number of atoms ionized in unit distance by N such photons (thus a parallel beam of such photons would, in travelling unit distance, suffer a fractional diminution μ_i due to that cause alone). The photons will, however, produce not only ionization but also excitation, specified by a coefficient μ_e (defined in exact analogy with μ_i), and of the photons absorbed in this way let a fraction μ_r/μ_e be re-emitted (as fluorescence) with energy still greater than 15 eV. In addition to α and the coefficients defined above, it is necessary to know r, the coefficient of reflexion of these photons at the electrodes; in this analysis, which is concerned only with the effects of photo-ionization, r will be assumed to be zero. The solution for the electron current L_-, due to Davidson, is given by the equation

$$L_- = \sum_{1,\,2,\,3} A_n \exp \alpha_n x \quad . \quad . \quad . \quad (5.7)$$

where the three values of α_n have the same dimensions as the primary ionization coefficient α, and are the three roots of the cubic equation

$$\alpha_n{}^3 - \alpha_n{}^2 n - \mu(\mu - \mu_r) + \mu\mu_i\{\theta + \alpha(\mu - \mu_r)/\mu_i\} = 0$$

where
$$\mu = \mu_i + \mu_e.$$

Inserting the boundary conditions in these equations, the three values of coefficient A_n are obtained from

$$A_1 + \psi A_2 + \phi A_3 = 0$$
$$A_1 + \psi_1 A_2 + \phi_1 A_3 = 0$$
$$A_1 + A_2 + A_3 = I_0$$

where the ψ's and ϕ's are expressions in terms of the coefficients and d. Solving these gives the solutions for A_1, A_2, and A_3, which all have the same denominator.

For certain values of the coefficients and at a certain distance d_s this denominator vanishes, that is

$$\phi\psi_1 - \phi_1\psi + \phi_1 - \phi + \psi - \psi_1 = 0 \quad . \quad . \quad (5.8)$$

The physical interpretation of this is that the current can increase indefinitely. This condition is the breakdown criterion. Expressed fully in terms of the various coefficients, this expression is

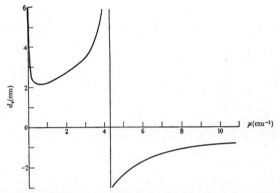

FIG. 5.8. Typical graph showing the variation of the sparking distance d_s with absorption coefficient μ (for conditions of no resonance fluorescence or degeneracy; $\theta = 0.042$; $k = 1.5 \times 10^{-3}$) [69]

not so simple as expression 5.2 relating to the other secondary processes.

5.4.3 *Significance of the Absorption Coefficients.* From this criterion (5.8) it is now possible to calculate the distance d_s at which breakdown will occur for any given set of conditions on the basis of given cross-sectional data. In order to see whether known values of the constants can lead to a physically significant solution the criterion will now be applied to the particular case of air, for which experimental data are available. As, however, some of the cross-sectional data are not entirely reliable, they have here been treated as parameters, and the computations carried out over a wide range of such parameters. A typical result for a simple case is given in Fig. 5.8, in which fluorescence and degeneracy are, for simplicity, ignored, and a simple absorption coefficient μ is taken instead. d_s is the distance at which breakdown will occur for any given value of μ. It readily follows that for the case of air in uniform fields there is only a limited range of absorption coefficient μ from zero to 4·2 over which breakdown is at all possible on the basis of photo-ionization; **negative** values of d_s have no significance. As μ approaches the limits

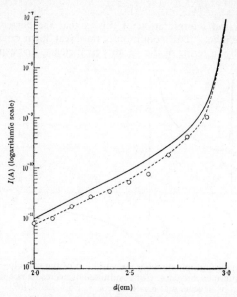

FIG. 5.9. Log I, d curve comparing the measured values (o) of the ionization currents I for air at $E/p = 40$ V/cm.mm.Hg with: (*a*) those obtained theoretically (—) assuming photo-ionization as the only secondary mechanism; (*b*) those obtained assuming a curve of the Townsend type (- - -), represented by equation (5.1). ($I_0 = 6 \times 10^{-15}$ A; $d_s = 2·94$ cm.) [69]

of this range (0 and 4·2) the sparking distance becomes infinite; and within this range there are two values of μ which give the same breakdown distance.

The curves which have been computed for the more complicated cases, which include resonance fluorescence and degeneracy, are similar, and in all these cases the values of the various coefficients of absorption necessary to give the observed sparking distance d_s are found to be not inconsistent with those observed experimentally. However, this condition alone, while necessary, is not sufficient to prove that photo-ionization is significant in breakdown, because the process must not only account for the breakdown distance, but it must also account for the observed growth of the pre-breakdown current which produces the breakdown. Consequently, the expression for the electron current I was evaluated for various values of x, and the curve drawn to show the development of the current across the gap. This is given in Fig. 5.9 by the full line.

The experimental data are presented by the points, and it is seen that although there is general agreement, there is a definite difference. On the other hand, it is seen that expression 5.1 can describe exactly the experimental data as shown by the dotted line going through the experimental points. It should be pointed out that both the full curve and the dotted curve have the same end-points, i.e., the same value of current at the cathode I_0 and the same sparking distance d_s. Lest the difference be taken to be due to lack of precise knowledge in the cross-sectional data, the full-line curve was evaluated for a wide range of such parameters, and it was found that a very wide range of such values had no significant effect on that curve.

5.4.4 *The Role of Photo-ionization.* An interesting case that might be considered here is when photo-ionization does take part as a secondary process but not a predominating part: i.e., when there are other secondary processes (e.g., γ or δ) acting at the same time. The analytical form of the curve, showing the growth of ionization under these conditions, reduces to a form very similar to 5.1, in which the part played by photo-ionization can be represented by another term η in the general expression for ω, which becomes

$$\omega = \beta + \alpha\gamma + \delta + \varepsilon + \eta . \quad . \quad . \quad (5.9)$$

but this only happens over a certain restricted range of μ's.

Another interesting fact about photo-ionization as a secondary process is that proof of its existence is no indication of its importance in breakdown. This follows from the restrictions on μ mentioned above.

It is therefore concluded from this analysis that for the range investigated:

(1) On the basis of present knowledge of atomic cross-sections photo-ionization can account approximately for the observed sparking distances in air. On the other hand, photo-ionization is not a probable secondary process in pure gases, because there is no process which is still a linear function of the

current, and which will give a sufficient number of high-energy photons.

(2) The photo-ionization process can, under certain restricted conditions, lead to a growth of pre-breakdown ionization currents in air, but the form predicted does not completely agree with that measured.

(3) Consequently, for the breakdown in air in uniform fields, cathode processes must be invoked; a conclusion which has been confirmed by the examination of electrode effects.

Further interesting conclusions concerning the way in which photons can act in the breakdown mechanism may be drawn from this analysis.

When photo-ionization was originally proposed [165] as an essential factor in the static breakdown mechanism in uniform fields it was stated on qualitative grounds that the absorption, and therefore the ionization, must take place *near* the head of the electron avalanche, as in that way a narrow filamentary spark channel would be produced. The present calculations show that, on the contrary, the amplification of the current by photo-ionization requires ionization *remote* from the avalanche head. The physical reason for this is the necessity for providing a long distance of travel for the electrons in the electric field to produce sufficient amplifications of the photo-electrons.

In those cases, when owing to the absence, for example, of any cathode effects, photo-ionization may be the only possible secondary process, then these calculations show that the general mechanism of breakdown is still the same as that involving other secondary processes, in that the effective photo-ionization tends to take place at points remote from the avalanche head, so regenerating the avalanche from behind; in fact, in the same way as the more efficient process of photo-electric emission from the cathode.

5.4.5 *Non-uniform Fields*. Breakdown in a non-uniform field is of great interest, and an example of this is found in the case of the lightning flash. It has been shown that qualitative considerations of the possible action of photo-ionization in breakdown can be misleading; this is especially so in the more complicated conditions of a non-uniform field. To find whether photo-ionization is an effective process in any particular case of non-uniform field breakdown, the complete quantitative calculations must be carried out for that field configuration, as has been done above for uniform fields. The above analysis in § 5.4 indicates the kind of data which are required to make these further investigations; in particular, precise knowledge of the dependence of the coefficients on the electric field, especially α, is required. The lightning flash has so far received only general qualitative treatment. Important information still needed (apart from the dependence of α on the electric field) is a precise knowledge of the distribution of the electric field in the neighbourhood of the thundercloud, in the important phase *just before the flash*, as well as knowledge of the physical conditions of the atmosphere.

It would appear that in uniform fields the photo-ionization term is generally a small fraction of the total general effect ω, so that η can be made to predominate only in conditions when the γ or δ terms are made small. Photo-ionization might be made to predominate at high pressures in uniform fields if the cathode surface is inactive, but it can more readily be done in non-uniform fields either by having a pointed cathode, so that the δ effect is negligible, or by having a pointed anode and the cathode very remote with γ and δ negligible. For the positive discharge from a point only the β and η secondary effects in the gas can act. There is, at present, insufficient evidence, especially of the β process, on which to assess the relative importance of the two effects in any given case. Accurate measurement of the growth of ionization currents is needed for the case of those non-uniform fields which are known accurately as a function of distance, so that computations may be made, using measured photo-ionization cross-sections, on the lines of those given above for uniform fields. Similarly the long gap is in general a particular case of a non-uniform field, and further experimental data are required on the same lines, for $pd \gg 1{,}000$ mm.Hg.cm. when it is possible that, even in a parallel-plate gap, the space charge due to the avalanche $\exp \int \alpha d$ may be sufficient to distort the field. This question still requires careful quantitative investigation.

CHAPTER VI

Breakdown under Extreme Conditions. Liberation of Electrons from Cold Electrode Surfaces

Electrical breakdown of a gas under extreme conditions of pressure or of gap distance d is of considerable practical importance: further, its elucidation involves problems of a theoretical nature. The following classes of breakdown will be discussed in this chapter: breakdown at (i) very high gas pressures; (ii) very short gap distance d; and (iii) very low gas pressure $\lesssim 10^{-5}$ mm. Hg, generally referred to, especially in industrial application, as vacuum breakdown.

6.1 Very High Gas Pressures

In recent years much consideration has been given to the use of gases at high pressure for the insulation of high voltages. The high-voltage electrodes of van de Graaf generators [96] and of X-ray tubes for deep-ray therapy have been insulated in this way. Further, the high-pressure gas insulation of cables in electrical power transmission is increasingly used in industrial areas.

The use of gas at high pressure in this way is based on Paschen's Law, which states that, for the usual collisional ionization and de-ionization processes, the breakdown potential is a function of the parameter pd only; i.e., a given voltage may be insulated by a small thickness d of gas dielectric provided the gas pressure is correspondingly high.

6.1.1 *Experimental Results.* Experimental investigations on the static breakdown of gases at very high values of the parameter $pd \gtrsim$ 10,000 mm.Hg.cm. have been carried out at the Massachusetts Institute of Technology [119, 249, 250, 286, 288]. These experiments, extending and generally confirming early work [262], show that Paschen's Law is not obeyed in this region; at the very high values of the parameter pd the breakdown potential is less than the value it would have if Paschen's law were obeyed. This result is illustrated by the results of Trump *et al.* shown in Fig. 6.1, in which the sparking potential is plotted against the pressure for various values of the parameter *pd*. Since the curves would be straight lines parallel to the pressure axis

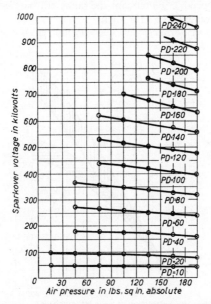

FIG. 6.1. Breakdown at very high gas pressures. The spark voltage in air as a function of pressure in pounds per square inch for constant values of pressure times gap distance. [288]

if Paschen's law were obeyed, the figure clearly shows that there are marked deviations from this law when $pd \gtrsim 20$ lb. /in. (2620 mm.Hg. cm.). Further results of these experiments are shown in Fig. 6.2, where the sparking field is plotted against pressure. These curves illustrate two points: first, that in this region of high values of the spark parameter *pd* the breakdown potential has no precisely defined value (there is a spread ~ 5–10 per cent in the experimentally observed values) and, secondly, there is a marked dependence of the breakdown potential on cathode material. It would appear to follow from these results that at the high values of *pd* an additional source of ionization comes into play, which is not operative with cold electrodes at lower values of $pd \lesssim 1,000$ mm.Hg.cm. That such a process may be due to the high value of the electric field may be seen from the following considerations. The electric field E in a 1-cm. gap at breakdown in air at atmospheric pressure is $\sim 3 \times 10^4$ V/cm. With a gas at pressure p of 100 atmospheres and a gap distance of 0·1 mm., the product pd remains the same, but the electric intensity E is now increased to $3 . 10^6$ V/cm.

6.1.2 *Influence of Electrodes.* The very high gas pressures at which

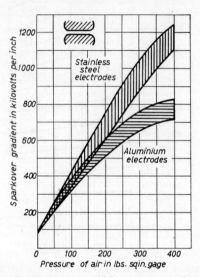

Fig. 6.2. Effect of cathode at very high gas pressure. Insulation strength of compressed air with stainless steel and with aluminium electrodes producing uniform fields over $\frac{1}{4}$, $\frac{1}{2}$, and $\frac{3}{4}$ inch gaps [286]

these phenomena occur would tend to lower the value of the secondary coefficient γ or δ/α; it follows that at these high electric fields (required by the high gas pressure) an additional ionization process comes into action, which must be very efficient and cathode dependent. Further, since Paschen's law is no longer obeyed, this new process cannot be any of the usual gas-collision processes. The explanation proposed by the investigators of this effect is that the Townsend type-mechanism, involving primary and secondary ionization processes α and ω/α in uniform fields, is assisted by a field-dependent electron emission

$$j = aE^2 \exp(-D/E)$$

from the cathode surface at electric fields $\gtrsim 10^5$ V/cm. although no detailed calculation of the mechanism was given. The occurrence of this process, dependent on the field E and not on the ratio E/p, would lead to deviations from Paschen's law. Moreover, since field emission will clearly depend on the nature of the cathode surface, the influence of the cathode on the breakdown potential is also readily understood.

A picture of the mechanism of breakdown at these high gas pressures can thus be drawn, provided it can be established that a field-dependent emission process can take place from cold-electrode surfaces in gases with electric fields $\sim 10^5$ V/cm. However, it is not easy to see how comparatively low fields of this order can produce adequate cold extraction of electrons from a cathode, because the Fowler–Nordheim theory (see § 3.11) requires fields about 100 times stronger than 10^5 V/cm. to produce significant cold emission from metals. This important point will be discussed below. An alternative attempt was made to account for the observed deviations from Paschen's law on the basis of the streamer [183] view in which the deviation from Paschen's law might be due to the action of space charges in the gas and not to the influence of the cathode. This theory predicted deviations in sparking potential of less than 1 per cent, which is much less than that observed, and which, as can be seen from Fig. 6.2, would be insignificant experimentally. Furthermore, on this view the breakdown potential would be independent of the nature of the cathode surface, and this is not in accordance with the experiments.

6.2 Very Short Gaps

6.2.1 *Contact Discharges at Make.* Very short sparks ($\sim 10^{-4}$ cm.) involving efficient ionization processes were reported by Earhart [72], and breakdown in shorter gaps ($\sim 10^{-7}$ cm.) with potentials ~ 1V were observed by Kinsley [130] and by Hobbs [113] in 1905. It was then noted that the sparks depended upon the nature of the electrodes; that the process was probably cold field extraction was suggested by J. J. Thomson [262].

Germer and Haworth [90, 92] have reported that when a condenser charged to about 50 V was connected to two cold electrodes which were brought to within about 10^{-4} cm. of each other, breakdown of the small gap occurred, and the condenser could be discharged through the ensuing spark. Such a discharge occurring between the contacts of a relay as used in communication engineering is considered by Germer to be an important cause of the erosion of the contact surface.

6.2.2 *The Mechanism: Influence of Electrodes.* In these cases of short gaps, since the breakdown potential of 50 V is well below the Paschen minimum ~ 300 V for air, some other ionization process, in addition to those represented by the coefficients α and ω/α, must be operative. It is significant that such a mechanism is cathode dependent and appears to become important when $E \sim 10^6$ V/cm. Application of the two basic requirements for electrical breakdown, viz., that there should be (i) initiatory electrons, and (ii) adequate amplification by ionization, raises the problem of the source of initiatory electrons and of the mechanism of the current amplification. When $d \sim 10^{-4}$ cm. the gap is too small for natural ionization of the gas to be always effective for producing initiatory electrons, and the short distance and low voltage (~ 50 V) leads to field intentities $\sim 10^5$ V/cm., which are too low to give effective cold extraction from pure metals on the Fowler–Nordheim theory (see § 3.11). To provide higher fields, $\sim 10^6$ or 10^7 V/cm., the electrodes would have to approach to within 10^{-6} cm., a distance which is less than the mean free path, and ionization by collision could not occur to the extent required to cause breakdown. Thus an adequate supply of electrons must be produced from cold electrodes under electric fields $\sim 10^5$ V/cm.

A significant feature of this type of breakdown is that the electrodes apparently must have a surface-contaminating film; a carbonaceous film, a fine layer of insulating dust particles or an oxide film appears to serve this purpose, but further investigation of this effect is necessary. When the electrode surfaces were of clean noble metals no discharge was obtained. Thus, it would appear that an explanation of breakdown in short gaps $\sim 10^{-4}$ cm. at voltages ~ 50 V is possible on the basis of the amplification of current by primary and secondary ionization only if some additional and efficient process of cold electron production from the cathode can occur with applied fields $\sim 10^5$ V/cm. Such a process would greatly enhance the value of the effective coefficient ω/α of secondary ionization at the cathode. This requirement is thus similar to that found necessary to account for breakdown at very high pressures.

6.3 Vacuum Breakdown

6.3.1 *Types of Breakdown.* A problem which arises in the operation of vacuum apparatus, such as a continuously evacuated electron-diffraction camera, is that internal insulating spaces sometimes break down with the passage of a spark when high potentials are applied to the electrode. The residual gas pressure in such apparatus may be $\lesssim 10^{-5}$ mm.Hg., and the mean free path of the gas molecules is of the order of the dimensions of the apparatus. Another type of breakdown can occur at very much lower pressures, at which the chance of an electron-molecule collision occurring in the gap is negligible: this is more truly 'vacuum' breakdown [149].

For breakdown to occur, two criteria must be satisfied: there must be suitably placed initiatory electrons, and a mechanism of ionization must occur to produce amplification of ions or electrons offsetting the loss by diffusion and drift in the inter-electrode space. For steady applied potentials the presence of initiatory electrons is to be expected, as natural ionization is sufficient in the usual large inter-electrode spaces.

Now, whether the well-known primary and secondary ionization processes represented by the generalized coefficients α and ω/α are themselves sufficient to produce breakdown depends on the value of the parameter pd, i.e., on the part of the Paschen curve, which represents the gas conditions in the given apparatus. The minimum of the Paschen curve occurs for most common gases for values of pd between about 0.1 and 1 mm.Hg.cm. (Chapter IV). For residual gas pressures $\sim 10^{-4}$ mm.Hg., and with inter-electrode distances ~ 1 metre, the product pd is $\sim 10^{-2}$ mm.Hg.cm. Although this is less than that corresponding to the Paschen minimum, nevertheless, it does not necessarily correspond to excessively high breakdown potential, and may be within the values found in practice (~ 50 kV) with such apparatus as X-ray and electron-diffraction cameras. Breakdown may then occur in accordance with the mechanism discussed in Chapter IV. Breakdown at the given potentials may be made more difficult or even prevented by reducing the parameter pd still farther, and this may be done either by further evacuation of gas or by reducing the inter-electrode distance.

The secondary ionization processes represented by the generalized coefficient ω/α may be classified in two groups: those dependent on the gas (β and η), and those dependent on the electrodes (γ and δ). Hence, evacuation of gas necessarily reduces the significance of the β and η processes, and true vacuum breakdown in those circumstances becomes dependent on electrode surface phenomena [46, 71, 287]. Before discussing this aspect, however, it is interesting to consider the influence of the application of magnetic fields to low-pressure apparatus and the consequent effect on the breakdown mechanism.

6.3.2 *Influence of Magnetic Fields.* Although, the maintenance of a small discharge current requires that the spark parameter pd must be sufficiently high, the presence of a magnetic field modifies the value of pd required.

Consider a longitudinal magnetic field H set up in the inter-electrode space. As electrons travel between cathode and anode their free paths between collisions are bent in accordance with the relation:

$$Heu = mv^2/r$$

and the lateral diffusion (see Chapter II) of the electron stream can be reduced, thus electron loss is reduced and the maintenance of the discharge facilitated. This applies to the case when the mean free path is smaller than the inter-electrode distance and gas collisions are significant. For lower pressures when the mean free path is of the order of, or greater than, the inter-electrode distance, the electrons are free in their passage between cathode and anode and their free paths become curved, and the lateral loss still reduced.

The case of a transverse magnetic field parallel to the electrode surface and thus at right angles to the electric field is interesting. Valle [289] considered the simple case when all free paths were assumed to be equal. The electron path, initially normal to the cathode, is bent by the magnetic field and returned to the cathode. The electron then does not progress towards the anode, its movement being confined to the space near the cathode. The motion is similar, then, to that under an equivalent pressure higher than that obtaining in the vessel, because the electrons now make more collisions with gas molecules than they would in the absence of the magnetic field. Valle's theory was not in accordance with experiment, but a more rigorous investigation was carried out by Somerville [252], who investigated the distribution of free paths about the mean value and electron reflection at the cathode, and his theory was more in accordance with experiment.

Thus a transverse magnetic field increases the ionization and leads to an increased effective gas pressure. The effect of this on the maintenance of a discharge depends, of course, on the actual magnitude of the pressure and on the parameter pd. For example, if pd is greater than that corresponding to the Paschen minimum, then the magnetic field effectively increases pd so that a higher breakdown potential is required. On the other hand, if pd in the evacuated vessel is less than that corresponding to the Paschen minimum, as is in general the case in vacuum apparatus, then the magnetic field, in effectively increasing pd, reduces the breakdown potential. Thus the influence of a magnetic field, as well as that of the electrode geometry, depends on the magnitude of the parameter pd.

These principles have been applied in the Philips gauge, which by utilizing this action of the magnetic field enables measurements of low pressures to be made from measurements of the electrical currents produced at the higher effective pressures.

6.3.3 *Influence of Electrode Surfaces.* The geometrical design of the electrodes, as well as the nature of their surfaces, can play an important part in facilitating breakdown at very low gas pressures. Geometrical irregularities, such as sharp edges or points, produce local concentration of the electric field, which may well attain values at which true field emission of electrons might occur (§ 3.11). Hence, to reduce the tendency to produce breakdown, all electrode surfaces should be smooth and as gently curved as possible. The microscopic surface geometry, as distinct from the shape of the whole electrodes, can produce local intensification of the field. The surface finish is important, as most worked surfaces are microscopically rough. Oxidation can also produce local roughness, and all such effects assist local intensification of the electric field, which in severe cases might lead to field emission. However, if cold emission from various electrode surfaces is to account for cases of observed internal flashover or breakdown, then it seems highly probable that the phenomena occur with electric intensities, even when locally enhanced, which are at least of an order of magnitude too low to be accounted for by field emission from pure metals. This, then, is a difficulty similar to those encountered in breakdown under the other extreme conditions considered above: at very high gas pressures, and at very short distances.

Thus, to develop a consistent and comprehensive theory of the mechanism of breakdown in gases applicable to all these cases, it is necessary to consider whether a process of cold emission of electrons can occur at ordinary electrode surfaces in gases when the macroscopic electric field applied is of the order of only $5 . 10^5$ V/cm., which is the value at which the phenomena discussed above in §§ 6.1, 6.2, and 6.3 appear to occur.

6.4 Liberation of Electrons at Cold Electrodes

6.4.1 *Experimental Method.* A convenient method of investigating electron production at electrodes of small gaps is based on the examination of the time lag of spark breakdown, originally used by Zuber [304] and von Laue [138]. (For full discussion see § 8.1 below.) With this method a comprehensive investigation in gases at high pressure was undertaken by Cobine and Easton [39], and more recently the method has been further developed [159] to examine electron emission from various electrode surfaces in different gases. The technique is illustrated in Fig. 6.3. A voltage $V \gtrsim 1.25\ V_s$ ($= AB$) is applied to a small parallel-plate gap comprised of the surface of interest for periods BC ($\sim 10^{-2}$ sec.), and in the absence of an

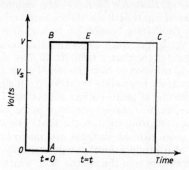

FIG. 6.3. Idealized over-voltage impulse

electron in the gap, V remains constant for time BC. If, however, an electron is liberated at the cathode at time t ($= BE$) a spark then occurs and V collapses. These events can be displayed on an oscilloscope and the time t recorded photographically, or alternatively, recorded on an integrating circuit. The process is repeated for a large number N of successive occasions. The time lag BE varies statistically, and in general is different for each successive voltage pulse of the same amplitude V. In a small gap with a sufficiently high field, each electron leads to a spark. Let the probability of an electron being liberated in any interval $t, t + \Delta t$ be $I\Delta t$, where I is assumed constant. The probability of the occurrence of a time exceeding t is then $\exp(- It)$, and the mean lag $\bar{t}$ is given by

$$I = 1/\bar{t} \quad . \quad . \quad . \quad . \quad . \quad (6.1)$$

Thus, I can be obtained by measuring a succession of such times. If n is the number of times in which the lag exceeds t in a large number N of trials, then the probability $\exp(- It)$ is n/N, i.e.,

$$I = (1/t) \ln(N/n) \quad . \quad . \quad . \quad . \quad (6.2)$$

so that I can also be obtained from the slope of the straight-line graph of $\ln(N/n)$ against t. This is the basis of investigations carried out at Swansea on electron emission.

6.4.2 *Experimental Results*. Metals in a variety of surface states were examined in the atmosphere [159, 154, 141, 189]. These included nickel, tungsten, iron, copper, and aluminium and alloys in different surface finishes such as oxidized, rolled, ground, or polished. Typical results in the form of ln (N/n), t curves showing the effect of altering the cathode surface are given in Fig. 6.4. The linearity of the

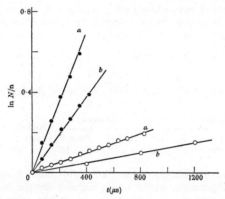

FIG. 6.4. Graphs of ln N/n against t. (*a*) Nickel cathode; (*b*) tungsten cathode; •, oxidized; ○, polished. $E = 10^5$ V/cm. [159]

graphs is in accordance with equation 6.2, and is consistent with the view that the probability of emission is constant under a given field.

Electron emission from nickel, iron, tungsten, Al-alloy, and copper electrodes in various surface states was measured, and it was shown that considerable emission rates $\sim 10^5 - 10^6$ electrons/sec. could be obtained when the applied electric field was as low as 10^5 V/cm. The emission was highly dependent upon the nature of the surface, its previous history, and the presence of dust particles or tarnish layers, etc. With highly polished cathodes, the emission was found to decrease rapidly from an initial value of $\sim 10^6$ electrons/ sec. to zero when the cathode was subjected to low-current sparking. Such a decrease in electrode activity had previously been noted by Howell [119] and others, and is usually referred to as conditioning or formation. It is attributed to the removal of dust particles and other sub-microscopic surface irregularities by erosion in the spark discharges of very low currents. The fact that surfaces from which the emission was negligible could be obtained by subjecting highly polished surfaces to low-current sparking was important in the development of the experimental technique, such electrodes providing a standard to which more active surfaces could be referred.

With heavily oxidized, dusty electrodes, an emission of $\sim 10^6$ electrons/sec. was obtained with an applied electric field of 2×10^5 V/cm., and removal of the dust produced a reduction by a factor of about 10^2 in the emission.

These experimental results show that different surfaces have different degrees of electrical activity, the physical state of the surface being more important than the underlying metal. Examples of emission rates from various surfaces in the atmosphere are given below in Table VI.

TABLE VI

Electron Emission in Electrons/sec. under Applied Fields
$\sim 10^4$ V/cm.

Steel			Copper		Nickel,	Al–Mg alloy,
Ground	Oxidized	Turned	Rolled	Turned	turned	turned
10^6	10^6	$5 \cdot 5 \times 10^3$	14×10^3	5×10^5	7×10^3	5×10^3

The existence of a field-dependent electron liberation from electrodes at room temperature, which would account for the properties of electrical breakdown under extreme conditions with fields $\sim 10^5$ V/cm. considered above (§§ 6.1, 6.2, and 6.3), is thus experimentally confirmed [155].

6.4.3 *Mechanism of Emission*. The dependence of the rate of emission upon the macroscopic applied electric field E was also investigated. The electrodes remained at room temperature and there was no evidence of maintained local hot-spots which could provide initiatory electrons thermionically, the emission phenomena appearing to be a cold process.

A typical family of ln (N/n), t experimental curves for oxidized nickel under different electric fields is shown in Fig. 6.5. From these curves, the slope of which gives I, the graphs of Fig. 6.6 have been obtained. These show that within the experimental error the relation between I and E is of the form

$$I = AE^2 \exp(-D/E) \quad . \quad . \quad . \quad (6.3)$$

Interpretation of the data on this emission offers some difficulty. That enhanced electron emission from a cathode could be produced by the presence of certain insulating films or powders has been known for some years. Schnitger [236] showed that such emission follows equation 6.3, but considered that the emission was produced only when the film lay on a non-metallic cathode of low conductivity. Equation 6.3 is analytically the same as the Fowler–Nordheim field-emission equation (see Chapter III) and shows that the process of electron production is field-dependent. This permits comparison of the experimentally determined relation 6.3 with the Fowler–Nord-

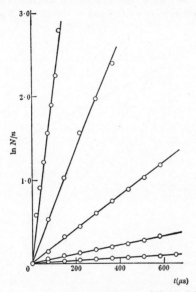

FIG. 6.5. Enhanced electron emission from oxidized nickel at different electric fields [159]

heim equation, which then allows estimates of the work function ϕ and emitting area S of the electron source to be made. The values $\phi \sim 0.5$ eV, $S \sim 10^{-14}$ cm.^{2} so obtained suggest that the electrons might be liberated from sites of molecular dimensions at the cathode surface, formed, possibly, by groups of negative ions. This view was supported by the fact that the presence of moisture affected the character of the phenomenon and ensured that the initial lag was short.

Emission from similar surfaces but *in vacuo* has also been investigated by Kerner and Raether [128], who showed that the emission followed the field law (6.3), on which basis $\phi = 5 \times 10^{-2}$ eV and $S = 6 \times 10^{-14}$ cm.^{2}. They point out, however, that the emission, which at constant temperature gives a linear log I, $\sqrt{E}$ relation with $\phi = 1.6$ eV and $S = 10^{-4}$ cm.^{2}, is equally or better described by the Schottky equation (Chapter III).

$$I = B \exp(-C\sqrt{E}) \quad . \quad . \quad . \quad . \quad (6.4)$$

It is clearly difficult to distinguish the mechanisms described by relationships as similar as 6.3 and 6.4 from the logarithmic plot,

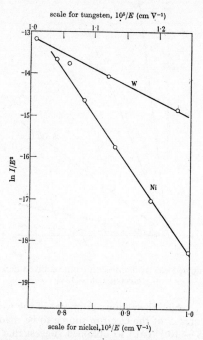

FIG. 6.6. Field dependence of I on E for oxidized nickel and oxidized tungsten electrodes [159]

but it is difficult to see how the mechanism described by 6.4 can account for the observed marked dependence on the presence of moisture in the time-lag experiments.

Emission from dry polished electrodes (with thin tarnish films in *dry* gases) was also examined at Swansea using the time-lag technique described above in § 6.4.1. It again appeared that the current

I was related to the field by equation 6.3. However, the values of ϕ and S deduced on the Fowler–Nordheim theory were too small to be of any physical significance, typical values being $\phi \sim 10^{-2}$ eV and $S \sim 10^{-20}$ cm.^{2}. Thus, the mechanism of emission was not the Fowler–Nordheim process. Application of the Schottky equation to these results leads to values of $\phi \sim 1.0$ eV, but requires a field enhancement ~ 10–10^2 when the electrode is assumed to be at room temperature: such enhancements with smooth surfaces are experimentally inadmissible.

In these conditions, there was always a long ($\sim$ secs.) initial lag before the first electron appeared. Once the first spark had occurred, however, subsequent sparks had short lags ($\sim 10^{-5}$ sec.) corresponding to considerably enhanced emission although the macroscopic fields were only $\sim 10^4$ V/cm. This effect is consistent with the view that a spark exerts an influence on the subsequent cathode emission of electrons.

It is probable therefore that positive ions produced in the first spark play an important role in the process of emission. If there were a thin ($\sim 2 \cdot 10^{-7}$ cm.) tarnish film at the cathode, the positive ions could set up for a short time a strong electric field across the film. The surface potential barrier retaining electrons inside the metal would then be distorted by the combined action of the positive-ion charge and the applied field and the escape of electrons facilitated.

It is interesting to note that a crude picture [154, 189] of such a distorted potential barrier can describe the emission while still assuming high values (~ 4.5 eV) for the work function of the metal.

The surface charge on the tarnish film may be reduced by allowing sufficient time between successive applications of the impulse electric field; this allows more time for leakage before the arrival of more ions produced in the next spark. When this is done the rate of emission is found to decrease considerably. Removal of the surface tarnish film by heating and bombardment with ions in a glow discharge also results in a great reduction in the emission, showing that the presence of the surface tarnish film is necessary to produce the enhanced emission. There is also a marked effect due to the nature and pressure of the gas for the cases of air, N_2, H_2, A, and He. These results are related to the work of Paetow [200] and Schnitger [236], and others [246, 140], on emission from electrode surfaces which had been subjected to various treatments, such as electron bombardment, or irradiation with ultra-violet light or X-rays.

Further work is necessary, however, in order to determine the precise form of the surface potential barrier and of the mechanism which produces the enhanced emission. Nevertheless, the experiments show that a considerable field-dependent liberation of electrons can take place at or from the surface of cathodes which are at room temperature. This process could be the further source of electrons required to account for the cases of electrical breakdown under extreme conditions discussed above. The introduction of this process thus generalizes, to high fields, the theory of breakdown depending on the development of ionization by primary and secondary processes [21, 155].

CHAPTER VII

Breakdown in Static Non-uniform Fields

7.1 General Considerations

So far, breakdown has been discussed for uniform fields in which the electric intensity is the same at both the cathode and anode. For asymmetrical electrode geometries the field is not the same at the two electrodes. The considerations of Chapters IV and V show that the field at the cathode is an important parameter when cathode electron emission plays a significant part in the breakdown process, as in many cases it does; consequently, asymmetric gaps will exhibit a polarity effect due to the asymmetry of the field in addition to any due to a difference in the nature of the electrode surfaces themselves. Electrode systems of some practical interest are those of a wire and co-axial cylinder (an overhead power cable is an extreme case of this), and of a pointed electrode at some distance from another conductor. The discharge which takes place in, say, the wire-cylinder configuration sometimes takes the form of a glow around the wire, often called a corona discharge. It will be shown that such systems present considerable problems in attempting to elucidate the mechanism of breakdown.

In an experimental investigation it is preferable to consider an asymmetrical electrode system in which the inter-electrode field distribution can be readily calculated. A too rapid radial change of field intensity should be avoided, otherwise the electrons do not attain a mean energy in a given element of space which can be specified only by the value of the electric field at that element (cf. § 2.7), making quantitative assessment of the experimental data difficult. In uniform fields the generalized coefficients α and ω/α have been measured for many gases with ionization currents which do not distort the field, and they are thus known as functions of E: $\alpha/p = f(E/p)$; $(\omega/\alpha) = \phi(E/p)$, at various pressures. Quantitative treatment of, say, the growth of current with distance d, as discussed above in Chapter IV, and of the temporal growth, as discussed below in Chapter VIII, can then be made for such uniform fields. With highly non-uniform fields, on the other hand, this cannot easily be done until functions such as

$$\alpha/p = f(E_r/p) \; ; \quad \omega/\alpha = \phi(E_r/p)$$

are obtained experimentally for non-uniform fields. It has long been realized that, from a sharply pointed conductor, especially at the higher gas pressures, the current can be so concentrated at the point that the current density here may be high enough to distort the field, and thus make estimation of α and ω/α difficult [274]. The parameter E/p is thus not known exactly along the ionization path. This is one reason why it is difficult to draw quantitative conclusions about the underlying ionization growth mechanism from the large amount of experimental observations on the numerous and varied phenomena obtainable with electrode geometries of the point-to-plane type [180]. At present the breakdown potential, or the potential required to maintain a very small current from an isolated sharply pointed conductor, cannot be expressed in a form which can be compared with the experimental measurements. However, interesting experimental work on ionization growth in highly-divergent fields has been undertaken in recent years [85, 191, 125].

When the point is positive and the cathode very remote, cathode processes play a negligible role; secondary ionization then consists of gas processes of which photo-ionization (η) and ionization by collision by positive ions (β) are the most likely. These, however, are the secondary processes about which the necessary quantitative data is at present lacking. Basic experimental data in this field are greatly needed, and should include precision measurements of the spatial growth of current in static fields and of temporal growth in impulse fields with low overvoltages (see Chapter VIII), determination of significant ionization coefficients, and the cross-sections for ionization by photons and by collision by positive ions; further, the experimental data must be obtained for different currents and with different gases, including mixtures, in which there may be reason to believe the requisite high-energy photons can be produced (see Chapter V).

When the point, or smaller electrode, is the cathode, the phenomena can be very complicated. The importance of secondary emission is increased by the fact that the field is intense at the point itself, thus enhancing the significance of the γ effect; further, the micro-state of the surface of the cathode can become exceedingly important (Chapter IV, § 4.8, and Chapter VI, § 6.4). Moreover, the nature of the gas itself has an influence on the surface state of the point (see § 6.4.2); the presence of oxygen or water vapour readily influences the formation of oxides or other tarnish films on the pointed cathode, especially when a high ion-current density also occurs there. It is obvious, too, that in addition to the effects of water vapour, the formation of nitrogen compounds by collisions in the electron avalanche can affect the cathode surface.

Unless the cathode is outgassed and free from tarnish films, and the gas pure, large local variations of γ, for instance, are to be expected, leading to correspondingly large variations in the ionization currents, so dependent on γ. Effects of lateral diffusion also become modified; and together with effects due to space charges in regions of high current density at the point, they can produce some con-

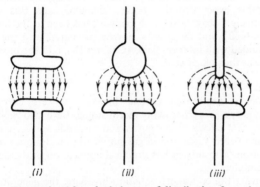

FIG. 7.1.—Illustration of gradual change of distribution from the uniform field to the highly non-uniform field

striction of the spark. For such reasons it is very difficult to draw conclusions of fundamental significance from experiments carried out with undegassed electrodes in a gas like air.

The considerable difficulties encountered in attempting to obtain a qualitative explanation of breakdown from, say, relatively small or pointed electrodes in air represent another example (§ 5.3.1) of how cases of technological interest are not necessarily those most readily investigated from the point of view of fundamental physics. It is thus hardly surprising that no quantitative explanation of the mechanism giving rise to the varied and variable phenomena of glows and intermittent sparks or streamers observed in such conditions has been put forward. In the following sections consideration is given to those cases of electrode geometry more suitable for fundamental investigation, and with gases of nature and purity more under control.

As indicated by Fig. 7.1 (i), (ii), and (iii), the case of a non-uniform field may be reached by a gradual transition from the uniform field case for which the breakdown mechanism has been elucidated up to $pd \sim 1000$ mm.Hg.cm. Since the ionization processes are continuous functions of the field, the transition, from say (i) to (iii), would be likely to produce a gradual change in the relative significance of the various secondary ionization processes taking part in the same general mechanism, rather than a fundamental change in the mechanism itself. In the important case of the wire and co-axial cylinder, when the radial change of electric field is such that the values of ionization coefficients in the various regions may be taken as approximately corresponding to the values of E/p in those regions, considerable experimental data are available, and this may be quantitatively assessed. Most of the work has been at the lower gas pressures [160], and the results may be compared with the similar data obtained with uniform fields (Chapter IV), and the breakdown mechanism thus elucidated.

7.2 Low Pressures

7.2.1 *Theory*. Studies of corona breakdown were carried out many years ago [274], but many recent studies have also been made. The important effects of gas purity and electrode surface condition require improved vacuum and gas-purification techniques for their investigation. The subject has practical application in the design of Geiger counters.

By solving the continuity equation involving the generation and drift of electrons and ions, Townsend [274], on the basis of the principles of ionization current growth given in Chapter IV, showed that the condition that a very small current maintains itself in a non-uniform field along a path between electrodes a and b, when expressed in the present generalized notation for cathode processes, is

$$1 - \omega/\alpha \left\{ \exp \int_a^b \alpha_r' dr - 1 \right\} = 0 \; . \quad . \quad . \quad (7.1)$$

where α_r' is the ionization coefficient radius r where the field is E_r and ω is assumed practically independent of r. For the co-axial cylinders of radius a and b of Fig. 7.2, the breakdown potential V_s is given by

$$E_r = V_s/r \ln (b/a) \; . \quad . \quad . \quad . \quad (7.2)$$

and, practically,

$$\omega/\alpha = \exp \left\{ -\frac{V_s}{\ln (b/a)} \int_{(E/p)_b}^{(E/p)_a} \frac{\alpha_r'/p}{(E/p)^2} \cdot \frac{dE_r}{p} \right\} \quad . \quad (7.3)$$

giving the dependence of V_s on ω/α. Equation 7.1 is the equivalent for non-uniform fields of equations 4.3 of Chapter IV for uniform fields.

It is interesting to note that non-uniformity of field may be produced, not only by an asymmetrical electrode system, but also by

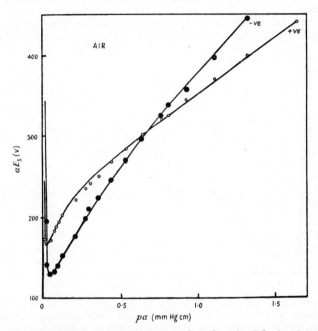

Fig. 7.2. The full-line curves give values of aE_s for tube C for breakdown with the wire positive (positive breakdown) and for the wire negative (negative breakdown). White and black circles give values of aE_s for positive and negative breakdown respectively in the geometrically similar tube B. The Similarity Theorem is obeyed, thus confirming equation 7.2, since (b/a) is the same for the two tubes [160]

the occurrence of a space charge in the gap. For example, if a sufficiently high value of I_0 were used, even in a parallel-plate gap, the space charge when the amplified current I is high may distort the field; this, however, does not necessarily change the breakdown mechanism: the criterion equation 7.1 can still be used, based on the action of primary and secondary processes; but in that case the ionization coefficients α and ω/α would naturally be functions of position. It might well happen that the value of V_s required to satisfy equation 7.1 would then be different from that in the case of a uniform field.

It is possible from equations 7.1 and 7.2 to make deductions which may be compared with experimental results and thus check the theory.

7.2.2 *Paschen's Law : Polarity Effect.* In the first place, a polarity effect is to be expected with non-uniform fields because the field has

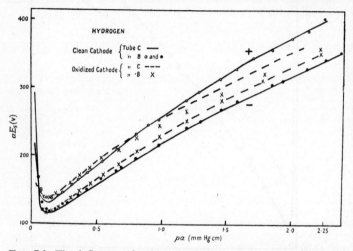

FIG. 7.3. The influence of oxidation of the cathode on the Similarity Theorem. The theorem is obeyed for both positive and negative breakdown when the electrodes are clean. When the electrodes are oxidized the theorem is not obeyed exactly for positive breakdown [160]

different values at the two electrodes. When the wire is negative the efficient cathode emission γ process is operative in a higher field intensity than when the cylinder is the negative. This is confirmed by experiment. Fig. 7.2 gives typical Paschen curves for air [160]. Since from 7.2, $V_s = aE_s \ln (b/a)$ where E_s is the field at the wire at breakdown and a and b are constants for a given electrode system, it is often convenient to plot E_s instead of V_s against the spark-parameter ap. In pure monatomic gases the curves for the wire negative are lower than those for the wire positive [160, 203]. When traces of impurity are present, however, Penning [203] has shown that the curves can intersect, a result attributed to the Penning Effect of collisions of the second kind involving metastable atoms (see § 3.4). The explanation of the relative values of V_s for positive and negative breakdown depends on the identification of the particular secondary ionization processes (β, γ_i, δ) predominant in the breakdown mechanism. Similar curves are obtained with air [160] and nitrogen [18]. This polarity effect is accentuated by increasing the non-uniformity of the field, and the point-to-plane configuration can in fact be used to rectify alternating potentials.

7.2.3 *The Similarity and Corona Relationships*. In non-uniform fields the similarity relation can be expressed as

$$V_s = aE_s \ln (b/a) = F(ap) \quad . \quad . \quad . \quad (7.4)$$

where E_s is the field at $r = a$ at breakdown; the relation is obeyed provided that only processes which are functions of E/p play any significant part in breakdown. Data have been obtained from three configurations A, B, and C of rod and co-axial-cylinder nickel electrodes in the same gas. The linear dimensions of B were twice those of C; while the rod of A had the same diameter as that of C, but the same cylinder diameter as B. Fig. 7.3 shows that with clean electrodes the breakdown potentials for tube C at a given value of p are the same as those for the geometrically similar tube B of double the linear dimensions but at half the gas pressure, for both the positive (o) and negative (•) breakdown. Thus the similarity principle is obeyed with clean electrodes, and the ionization and de-ionization processes predominant in the breakdown are functions of E/p. Fig. 7.2 shows that the principle is obeyed in air also.

In a different co-axial system with a wire of the same radius a but different cylinder radius b', the potential V_s' at breakdown is given by a relation similar to 7.4, viz.:

$$V_s' = aE_s \ln (b'/a),$$

so that assuming E_s is the same in the two systems

$$V_s'/V_s = \ln (b'/a)/\ln (b/a) \quad . \quad . \quad . \quad (7.5)$$

This is the corona relation, enabling the breakdown potential for a cylindrical system b', a to be calculated when that for the system b, a is known. The data given in Fig. 7.4 verify the corona relation 7.5 for hydrogen.

From this it now is deduced that the value of the field at a small distance from the rod determines the breakdown process. When $b >> a$, the value of E/p at b may become negligible, and then processes in that region will have little effect on the maintenance of a

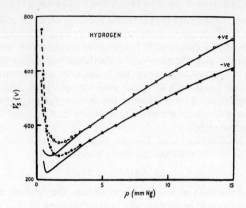

FIG. 7.4. The measured values (white and black circles) of V_s for tube C are compared with those (curves) calculated from the measured values for tube A using the corona relationship [160]

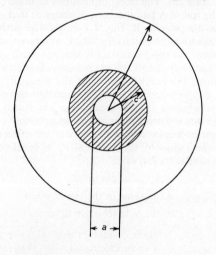

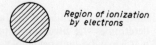

Region of ionization
by electrons

FIG. 7.5. Region of ionization by electrons between co-axial cylinders

120

small current. The small cylindrical volume co-axial with the wire is the region in which all ionization takes place (Fig. 7.5); in the space between the outer boundary of this region and the cylindrical electrode the motion of the electrons is determined mainly by diffusion and drift, and no ionization by collision occurs there because E/p there is low. Thus, provided the potential of the outer conductor is sufficient to maintain the required field intensity in the critical region around the wire, the actual location of that outer electrode is not important. The corona relation also holds in air and in pure helium [160].

7.2.4 *Effect of Impurities.* Impurities have a marked effect on the corona breakdown potential in monatomic gases [160, 203], and the case of helium is illustrated in Fig. 7.6. As the impurities were progressively removed the breakdown potential rose and the values of ω/α fell; the similarity relationship held only in the purest specimens of helium. These results are consistent with the view that a significant ionization process in the presence of impurities is due to collisions of the second kind (§ 3.4), and that the positive ions produced were mainly those of the impurity gas.

7.2.5 *Secondary Ionization Processes.* Consider now the actual value of ω/α deducible from 7.3 in the case of H_2, for comparison with those deduced in the same way from breakdown in a uniform field (Chapter IV). These are given in Fig. 7.7, and are based on values of α given by Ayres [11].

For clean Ni electrodes, Fig. 7.4 shows that the corona-similarity relationships holds. Consequently the primary ionization process is a single impact α process and the secondary process depends on E/p, i.e., it depends on energies of ions and electrons. When the cylinder was the cathode, secondary emission could be due to incidence of photons and positive ions; Fig. 7.7 shows a rapid increase of ω/α with E/p from 10^{-3} at 15 V/cm.mm.Hg. to 6×10^{-2} at $E/p = 150$ V/cm.mm.Hg. On the other hand, when the wire was the cathode, photo-electric emission could not play any predominant role (owing to its relatively small area), and Fig. 7.7 shows that ω/α steadily increased with E/p from small values ($\sim 10^{-3}$) at $E/p = 150$ V/cm.mm. Hg. to high values ($\sim 6 \cdot 10^{-2}$) when $E/p \sim 1000$ V/cm.mm.Hg. This is consistent with the action of positive ions of hydrogen whose energy steadily increases in this range of E/p.

Consider now the rapid increase of ω/α at the low values of E/p when the cylinder was cathode. Clearly, this was not due to incidence of positive ions (γ), because when E/p was 150 V/cm.mm.Hg. and the wire negative (and photo-electric emission negligible), ω/α due to

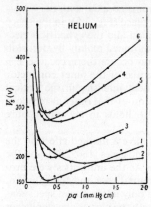

Breakdown potentials of helium in various stages of purification for tube C. 1, 3 and 5 negative wire; 2, 4 and 6 positive wire

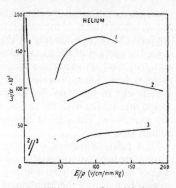

(ω/α, E/p) curves for nickel electrodes and helium in various stages of purification. 1, high concentration of atoms of impurity; 2, lower concentration of atoms of impurity; 3, helium in the final stages of purification

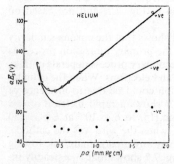

The full curves give values of aE_s for tube C for positive and negative breakdown. Points (white and black circles) give values of aE_s for positive and negative breakdown in the geometrically similar tube B. The similarity theorem is obeyed for positive breakdown but not for negative

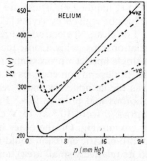

The measured values (white and black circles) of V_s for tube C are compared with these (curves) calculated from the measured values for tube A using the corona relationship

FIG. 7.6. [160]

122

ions alone (γ) was small ($\sim 10^{-3}$). The rapid increase to the high values ($\sim 10^{-1}$) when the cylinder was cathode and E/p low is interpreted as due to photons [147, 150] (see Chapter IV). The dotted line in Fig. 7.7 gives the values of ω/α obtained with Ni electrodes, taking the values of α due to Ayres, in H_2 in a uniform field (Chapter IV) when only about half the total number of photons could fall on the cathode; in the corona case practically all the photons fall on the

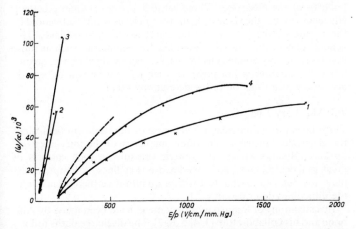

FIG. 7.7. ω/α, E/p curves for hydrogen and nickel electrodes in various states. Curves 2 and 3 obtained with the cylinder as cathode; curves 1 and 4 obtained with the wire cathode. For 1 and 2 the electrodes were oxidized; for 3 and 4 they were clean

cylinder. For $E/p \lesssim 150$ V/cm.mm.Hg. the agreement is satisfactory, considering the difficulty of calculating ω/α from 7.3.

It is significant to note that in purified H_2, but with electrodes covered with oxide layers and $E/p \lesssim 35$ V/cm.mm.Hg., the similarity relation was not obeyed for a wire anode; at high values of E/p, however, the relation held. On the other hand, with wire cathodes, the similarity held always. In the former case it follows that an ionization process not dependent on E/p played a part: this was not due to possible impurities in the gas and was an electrode effect (see Chapter VI). Similar considerations apply to results in H_2, air (a mixture) and pure He (a monatomic gas).

The conclusion can then be drawn that the breakdown mechanism in non-uniform fields at these lower gas pressures is in accordance with the theory expressed in equations 7.1, 7.2, and 7.3, provided that the field variation with distance is not too great. The mechanism is the result of primary and secondary ionization processes: a number of such processes, e.g., secondary emission due to incidence of positive ions (γ) or photons (δ), can and do occur, and the relative values of the breakdown potential V_s for positive and negative wire are determined by the relative importance of the various secondary processes acting, which is itself determined by the geometry and polarity of the electrodes. These cathode processes differ greatly in efficiency, so that the value of V_s in static fields is greatly influenced by the nature of the cathode surface, just as in uniform fields. This general conclusion must be modified for geometries such as those involving sharply pointed electrodes, for, as explained above, quantitative explanation is not possible when α is not known sufficiently accurately as a function of the field at any point.

7.3 The Very Long Gap

The long gap is, in practice, often a case of non-uniform field, since the electrode dimensions are often smaller than the inter-electrode distance. Breakdown at atmospheric pressure in such cases is of great practical interest, e.g., overhead power lines. Attempts to explain the detailed mechanism with a quantitative theory encounter the difficulties described in § 7.1.

Investigations of long-spark phenomena have been made by Allibone and his collaborators [3, 4, 5, 6, 7]. The discharge paths following breakdown have been photographed, and the tracks are often seen to be forked. It has been suggested that this forking is a basic property of the mechanism, but equally it could be due to fortuitous variations in the gap conditions (pressure, temperature, dust) which are extremely likely to occur in long gaps in conditions incompletely controlled. Such a forked path in the non-uniform field at the edges of the electrodes is illustrated in Plate II obtained by Bruce [32], but it is significant that in a uniform field with more controlled conditions, Plate I shows the spark track to be practically straight, as expected on the basis of simple progression of an electron avalanche along the field. The value of the spark parameter pd in the case of long gaps is $\gtrsim 10,000$ mm.Hg.cm. and no quantitative data of growth of the pre-breakdown current is as yet available for this range; the maximum value for which such data are available being 1200 mm.Hg.cm. (Chapter V). No quantitative calculations on ionization growth have yet been published on the basis of the most likely secondary processes of photo-ionization or of ionization by collision by positive

PLATE I

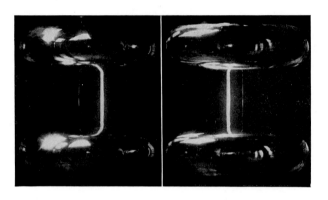

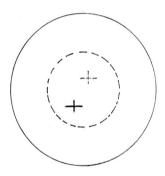

Uniform-field spark-over, 6 cm. spacing,
upper electrode positive

PLATE II

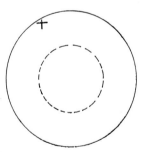

Non-uniform-field spark-over, showing stepped path.
8.7 cm. spacing. No filter. Upper electrode positive

ions. To test any quantitative theory of the breakdown such calculations must be made, possibly on the lines of that for photo-ionization in the uniform field case discussed in Chapter V, § 5.4.

In the present state of knowledge of cross-sectional data it is not possible to assess the relative importance of ionization by photons or by positive ions, the question still being open; nevertheless, one observation can still be made. The quantitative analysis of the growth of pre-breakdown current due to the action of photo-ionization as a secondary process which has been made for a uniform field (Chapter V) indicates how this process makes its contribution. Amplification is the more effective the more the photons penetrate backwards towards the cathode, since in those circumstances the maximum contribution is then made by the ionization avalanches initiated by the photo-electrons. To a smaller extent lateral penetration of the photons has a similar effect. These effects give rise to a widening of the main avalanche. On the other hand, the action of positive ions, if they ionize by collision, is more local to the main avalanche, which can then more easily remain a narrow track. This conclusion is contrary to the suggestion that photo-ionization is a necessary process in order to produce a narrower track than is to be expected on the basis of a Townsend-type mechanism depending on other secondary processes. The source of the required high-energy photons, if photo-ionization is the predominant secondary process in long gaps, is still an outstanding problem. The analysis given in Chapter V shows that such photons can be produced in air, and photo-ionization in the absence of a suitably disposed cathode is therefore a quite possible secondary process in that gas. The case of other gases is, however, far from clear.

Another factor requiring experimental investigation and quantitative assessment is the possible field distortion in long gaps due to the positive ion content of the electron avalanche ($e^{\alpha d}$) when d is very large [213, 216]; any local increase of field would enable the primary (α) and secondary process (ω/α) to proceed at an enhanced rate. It may be pointed out here that one of the outstanding needs for the quantitative elucidation of the breakdown of a long gap is that of precise values of α/p and of E/p in such cases.

Investigations of long gaps (including lightning) have been made by Norrinder [195, 196] and his colleagues in Sweden, from which they have concluded that all present theories fail to explain breakdown in this range, and that the process cannot yet quantitatively be accounted for. These authors also draw attention to the importance of the dark phase (i.e., pre-breakdown growth) in the initial process of the breakdown mechanism—which is not recorded in photographs of the luminous tracks of the spark. It is pointless, at present, to put forward views or theories for these particular cases of long gaps until the required experimental data are forthcoming.

A space charge could reduce the effective gap length to be broken by practically dividing the total gap into separate sections. A similar effect, of course, takes place in the transition from breakdown to a self-maintained discharge by the effect of the accumulation of positive ions near the cathode surface, on the lines indicated by Townsend [274, 268].

Many experimental calibrations of long-gap breakdown, using spherical electrodes, have been made, notably by Stephenson [254] and by Whitehead [296]. Precision measurements with uniform fields in long gaps between parallel-plate electrodes of Stephenson profile have been made by F. M. Bruce [30], who found that the peak a.c. breakdown voltage can be stated as:

$$V = 24.22d + 6.08\sqrt{d}\ \text{kV}.$$

at 20° C. and 760 mm. Hg, where d is in cm. Later work by Bruce and his colleagues in Glasgow has shown that the uniform field gap is superior to the sphere gap for calibration of high-impulse voltages, being less dependent upon external irradiation, or conversely, more stable for a given degree of irradiation, and also showing little dependence upon polarity.

Mention must also be made of the most spectacular example of long-gap electrical breakdown—the lightning discharge. Schonland and his colleagues [237, 238, 239, 240, 241] in South Africa and McEachron [168] in the United States have made comprehensive experimental analyses of discharge strokes using a modification of the Boys camera. Such work has been most useful in demonstrating the nature of the discharges, but it is not easy from such data to elucidate the actual mechanism which produces the initial phases of the breakdown, a difficulty which is inherent in any investigation based on photographic recording of any light produced by a considerable current. Much work has been done, however, in elucidating the forms of the discharge itself and the reason for the behaviour of the different kinds of strokes [9]. Photography of discharge tracks in long gaps can, however, be helpful in recording the spatial–temporal growth of ionization along the whole path (see Chapter VIII). Apart from the difficulties (see § 7.1 above) inherent in investigating the long gap in a non-uniform field, the case of lightning has further difficulties, since the actual discharge conditions are not controlled or known precisely. The forked nature of the stroke may well be explained by small local changes in atmospheric conditions, and such shapes can be produced in the laboratory (see Plate II). The condition for the transition of the initial ionization avalanche with a visible, apparently self-propagating stroke, has been discussed by C. E. R. Bruce [27, 25, 26, 29] and others [129, 205, 301]. Bruce concludes that the necessary criterion is the attainment of a critical current ~ 0.5–1 amp. When this is attained, arc-like conditions in the spark track occur, and sufficient current is generated along the spark track to make good the lateral corona-like loss from the track. This criterion may well be applicable more generally to cases of long non-uniform field gaps. It had previously been assumed that the average electric field along the path before breakdown was $\sim 10^4$ V/cm., whereas more recently it has been found that the field is nearer 100 V/cm. The value of the field in the atmosphere prior to breakdown is a matter of great importance, and accurate values are needed on which to base theories of the process.

CHAPTER VIII

Temporal Growth of Ionization

8.1 Impulse Breakdown; Initiatory Time Lags

In this monograph, so far, theoretical and experimental investigations of the mechanism which sets the criterion for electrical breakdown have been discussed for both uniform and non-uniform but static electric fields, i.e., for pre-breakdown currents in the steady state, the factors α and ω/α being constant in time. The considerations of Chapter IV show that the original Townsend theory was concerned with precisely those conditions. Indeed, with the techniques available in the early part of the century no other conditions could easily have been investigated; the sources of potential were usually batteries of cells, and these were steady. The Townsend criterion for static breakdown is a limiting case in such circumstances. In practice, breakdown under impulsive fields is of a very great importance, particularly in high-voltage engineering, and its investigation raises some interesting problems [123]. These concern: (i) the provision of initiatory electrons; and (ii) the consequences of the finite rate of the temporal growth of current after the criterion for static breakdown has been satisfied.

The considerations in Chapter IV show that unless an initiatory electron is provided, electrical breakdown cannot occur, because an avalanche cannot then be started. In the case of slowly varying fields there is usually no difficulty in finding an initiatory electron from natural sources, e.g., cosmic rays, detachment from gaseous ions, etc. Under impulsive fields this is not always the case, and for pulses of short duration, depending on the gap volume, natural sources may not be able to provide an initiatory electron in the small time interval during which the pulse is applied, and in the absence of any other source breakdown would not then occur. The time t, which elapses between the application of a potential difference $\geqslant V$, to the spark gaps and the appearance of a suitably placed initiatory electron is called the statistical or initiatory time lag of the gap, the appearance of such electrons being usually statistically distributed.[1] After the provision of such an electron, the time t_f required by the ionization processes to generate a current of any given magnitude which may be used to specify the breakdown of the gap (as indicated, for example, by the collapse of gap voltage) is known as the formative time lag. The sum $t_f + t_s$ is known as the total spark lag t (§ 6.4.1).

It is clear that for breakdown to occur at the lowest breakdown potential during a very brief voltage pulse the cathode must be adequately irradiated in order to supply sufficient suitably placed

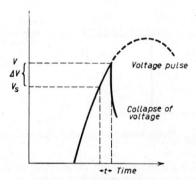

FIG. 8.1. Breakdown on a rising wave-front of voltage

electrons, and this may be done by ultra-violet light from another spark or by the local presence of radio-active matter. In practice, however, it is often found that on the application of high impulse fields to a given gap, the statistical time lag is much less than would be expected on the assumption that the initiatory electrons were provided only from natural sources. The average time of production of electrons from cosmic rays will, of course, depend on the volume of the gas enclosed in the inter-electrode space. When this is small, as in the case of small gaps (e.g., 1-cm. parallel discs 0·5 mm. apart), it can be shown that the rate of production of electrons by natural sources [262] is certainly less than about 5 per sec. (i.e., $t_s < 0·2$ sec.). In such gaps values of $t_s \sim 10^{-5}$ have been observed [159], and experimental investigations described above in § 6.4 show that these electrons are liberated near the cathode by a mechanism dependent on the field E in the gap when $E > E_s$.

[1] When the mechanism of liberation of the initiatory electrons itself depends on the applied electric field, E must then be specified in specifying t_s.

I

Unless the magnitude of the applied potential V exceeds the static breakdown potential V_s, breakdown will not occur; and it is clear that with a rising wave of applied potential, the potential V at which the current reaches the required value for breakdown will occur at times after the value V_s is reached, depending on the total spark lag. This is illustrated in Fig. 8.1. The ratio V/V_s is sometimes called the impulse ratio, and this clearly depends on $t_s + t_f$ and the rate of growth of the applied potential. $V - V_s = \Delta V$ is called the over-voltage. These considerations are of importance in the design and

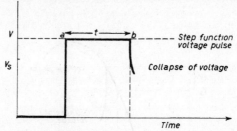

Fig. 8.2. Breakdown on a step-function voltage pulse

operation of electrical equipment, such as the sparking-plugs and distributors of the ignition system of internal-combustion engines. The impulse ratio of a cold spark-plug (engine starting from cold) may be as high as 2, while with a hot plug the impulse ratio may be as low as 1·1. In practice t_f is often very much smaller than t_s, in which case t_s can be determined simply by measuring t. However, to measure t_f accurately, t_s has to be eliminated, and this can be done by adequate irradiation of the cathode. Since t_f will depend on the ionization processes, which themselves depend on the field, it is usual in measuring t_f to specify a given field. This necessitates the use of a step function pulse as illustrated in Fig. 8.2 so that the field (and therefore α and ω/α) is constant while the current is growing. If the time of rise of the pulse voltage from zero to V is negligible (say, $\sim 10^{-8}$ sec.), then the total lag can be represented by the length of the pulse trace (a, b) before breakdown occurs, breakdown being indicated by the commencement of the collapse of the voltage. Such oscilloscope traces can be used to measure t_f.

8.2 Formative Time Lags

Systematic study of the electrical breakdown of an overvolted gap owes much to the work of Rogowski and others [247] since 1926.

Using impulse generators and cathode-ray oscilloscopes, spark time lags of the order of 10^{-8} sec. were observed for long gaps of the order of a cm. As explained above in § 5.1, the contrast of such times with the longer times expected was so great that it was at one time considered to throw doubts on the Townsend-type mechanism involving the primary and secondary processes in general. These doubts consequently led to the idea that some quite different, but extremely fast, process came suddenly into operation at potentials of V_s and greater. It is important to appreciate, at this stage, that that conclusion was not based on a quantitative analysis of the times to be expected from the action of a generalized Townsend ionization mechanism involving the various secondary processes in uniform fields described in Chapters IV and V. Before reliable conclusions can be drawn about the mechanism of breakdown from studies of formative times, it is necessary first to calculate theoretically what the time rate of growth of ionization is likely to be on the basis of a mechanism of current growth dependent on primary and secondary processes in uniform fields (when α and ω/α are known), and then to compare the calculated times with those observed. Sufficient attention has, unfortunately, not been paid in the past to this aspect, and the neglect has led to misconception concerning the significance of the magnitude of the formative time measured, and indeed, also to misconceptions about the physical significance of the criterion itself for breakdown in static fields.

Townsend's original theory was proposed for the static case in which α and ω/α are constants in the given field. It was shown in Chapter IV that a steady current can be self-maintained even when the initial current I_0 is zero, and this condition physically specifies V_s. When V attains the value V_s an instantaneous generation of a small finite number of electrons at the cathode will develop into a steady self-maintained current with I_0 zero; on the other hand, when I_0 is finite the current I in the gap will increase progressively with time (with a constant field) but not at an increasing rate. When $V > V_s$ the ionization increases progressively in time even when started only by an instantaneous generation of a small number of electrons, the rate of growth depending on the nature of the ionization processes and on the value of the coefficients (which all depend on E at a given p). The Townsend steady-state equations 4.1 and 4.2, Chapter IV, have no relevance to this impulse case.

Comparison of the observed rate of growth of ionization when $V - V_s$ is small with the result of calculations made on the basis of the known cathode processes γ and δ (which coefficients are all continuous functions of V), enables the relative significance of these processes to be assessed for the conditions almost when the breakdown criterion $V = V_s$ is satisfied. The investigation can thus provide important information as to the secondary ionization processes operative in setting the criterion for static breakdown when $V = V_s$.

8.3 Theory of the Growth of Ionization

8.3.1 *General Principles*. The time rate of development of ionization will depend on the particular secondary processes operative. For example, secondary ionization produced by photo-electric action at the cathode depends on the mobilities of electrons only (the transit time of the photons being negligible when fluorescence is negligible), and this is a faster process than one involving the incidence of positive ions on the cathode, because of the much lower mobilities of positive ions ($W_+/W_- \sim 10^{-2}$, Chapter II). Thus, measurements of the time interval elapsing between the appearance of the initiatory electron in the gap and the attainment of a given value of ionization current in a uniform constant field should help to distinguish between the various possible secondary ionization processes. Although it can readily be seen from general considerations that an increase of ΔV will produce a decrease of t_i, it is, however, not immediately obvious how the quantitative relation expressing t_i in terms of ΔV depends on the particular secondary process operating.

Since the predominance of the cathode processes γ and δ has been established (Chapter IV) the ε, β, and η processes may be neglected in the following analysis of the temporal development of ionization in a uniform field: it is assumed that the only significant electron-production process in the gas is due to the α process. In the non-steady state ($V > V_s$), α will exceed the value obtaining at $V = V_s$, since α/p is a function of V/pd.

Schade [233] and Steenbeck [253] made calculations of the temporal growth of ionization by considering build-up by successive avalanches developing by means of the α and γ processes. Later Bartholomeyczyk [13] considered the growth based on the α, γ, and δ processes, starting from the differential equations describing the motions of electrons and ions. These continuity equations are:

$$(\partial I_-/\partial t)/W_- = - \partial I_-/\partial x + \alpha I_- \quad . \quad . \quad (8.1(a))$$

and

$$(\partial I_+/\partial t)/W_+ = + \partial I_+/\partial x + \alpha I_- \quad . \quad . \quad (8.1(b))$$

where I_- and I_+ are the electron and positive-ion currents at a distance x from the cathode at a time t; as boundary conditions he used

$$I_-(o, t) = \gamma I_+(o, t) + \delta \int_0^d I_- e^{-\mu x} dx \quad . \quad (8.2(a))$$

$$I_+(d, t) = 0 \quad . \quad . \quad . \quad . \quad . \quad . \quad (8.2(b))$$

It will be noted that in equation 8.2(a) the externally maintained current I_0 is omitted. For calculating the current as a function of time and distance, Bartholomeyczyk gave the approximate solution

$$I_-(x, t) \exp(-\alpha x) = C \exp\{\lambda(t - x/W_-)\} \quad . \quad (8.3)$$

C is a constant and λ has a real value satisfying $F(d) = 0$, where

$$F(x) = 1 - (\alpha\gamma/\phi)(\exp\phi x - 1) - (\delta/\psi)(\exp\psi x - 1);$$
$$\phi = \alpha - (\lambda/W); \qquad \psi = \alpha - \mu - (\lambda/W_-);$$
$$1/W = 1/W_- + 1/W_+.$$

This solution both neglects I_0 and does not take correct account of (arbitrarily prescribed) initial distributions of charge in the gap. Owing to the neglect of I_0, this solution tends to zero with increasing time when $V < V_s$. With $V >> V_s$, however, the expression enables the current growth to be traced to a very rough approximation.

Davidson [55], working at Swansea, pointed out that Bartholomeyczyk's expression can be altered so as to satisfy both equations 8.1 and the correct boundary conditions incorporating I_0 (but still not the correct initial conditions) by using the following procedure. If λ is given Bartholomeyczyk's value, and if

$$P = 1 - \gamma(\exp\alpha d - 1) - (\delta/\alpha - \mu)\{\exp(\alpha - \mu)d - 1\}$$

then it can readily be shown that an expression

$$I_-(x, t) \exp(-\alpha x) = I_0/P + C \exp\{\lambda(t - x/W_-)\} \quad (8.4)$$

with an accompanying expression for I_+ satisfy equations 8.1 as well as the corrected boundary conditions. The expression 8.4 is Davidson's approximate solution of the problem. The constant C may be given a value which gives approximate agreement with the initial conditions; for example, if the initial value of $I_-(o, t)$ is c, the solution can be made to have that initial value of $I_-(o, t)$ by taking C as $c - I_0/P$. The best value C_0 to give it will be considered in the next section. The expression giving the current $I_-(o, t)$ at the cathode at time t is then, taking $\mu = 0$

$$I_-(o, t) = I_0/[1 - (\delta/\alpha + \gamma)\{\exp\alpha d - 1\}] + C_0 \exp\lambda t \quad (8.5)$$

where I_0 is the externally generated photo-electric current from the cathode. This solution, although approximate, is nevertheless adequate in many practical cases. It is least accurate for times t a small multiple of the electron transit time d/W_- of the gap, but becomes more accurate for longer times. The solution, however, never becomes exact, and for the greatest accuracy the exact solutions of the continuity equations must be used.

8.3.2 *Davidson's Exact Expressions for Ionization Growth.** Davidson has given an accurate solution of the continuity equations 8.1 in which the solution not only satisfies the continuity equation and the correct boundary conditions including I_0, but also satisfies the initial conditions completely. This solution gives any prescribed initial distribution of positive and negative charge in the whole range $x = 0$ to d at $t = 0$. Davidson's analysis will now be given.

The equation $F(d) = 0$ from which λ was calculated has, in addition to the real root, an infinite number of complex roots; the last term in equation 8.4 must therefore be replaced by a summation containing these various λ's and with C's determined by the initial conditions. The mathematical problem itself is of little interest; it will be sufficient here to state the final expressions obtained for I_- and I_+. This latter expression is of great importance in determining when the effects of space charge become significant.

It is convenient to think of the expression for, say, $I_-(x, t)$ as consisting of two parts: (i) the value which it would have if the initial charge distribution were absent; and (ii) the value which it would have if the constant generation I_0 were absent. The quantity $I_-(x, t)$ which will be present in the experiment is the sum of the two parts. The same remarks apply to $I_+(x, t)$. In the part (ii), $I_-(x, t)$ and $I_+(x, t)$ are conveniently calculated from the initial distribution, say, $\rho_- = f_-(x)$ and $\rho_+ = f_+(x)$, by means of four g's (Green's functions), of which, for example, $g_-^+ (xtx_1)$ is the $I_-(x, t)$ due to the presence at time zero of unit positive quantity in the region of $x = x_1$. Thus the required $I_-(x, t)$ of part (ii) is

$$\int_0^d \{g_-^- f_-(x_1) + g_-^+ f_+(x_1)\}dx_1 \quad . \quad . \quad . \quad (8.6)$$

and a corresponding expression gives $I_+(x, t)$.

For values of t less than x/W_- the values of g_-^+ and g_+^-, and also of the I_- and I_+ of part (i), are of a simple nature, readily seen on visualizing the motion. For example, g_-^- is zero in this range of time if $x < x_1$. If $x > x_1$ there is a sudden pulse at $t = (x - x_1)/W_-$,

* This section may be omitted by the undergraduate reader.

conveying a quantity $\exp \alpha(x - x_1)$. At all later times the series expressions given below for these quantities are valid. Similarly the values of g_-^+ and g_+^+ are readily seen at times up to $(x_1/W_+) + (x/W_-)$, after which the series are to be used. The series expressions are:

Part (i)

$$\begin{aligned}
I_-/I_0 &= \exp \alpha x/P + \Sigma Q \\
I_+/I_0 &= (\exp \alpha d - \exp \alpha x)/P + \Sigma RQ
\end{aligned} \Bigg\} \quad . \quad . \quad (8.7)$$

where

$$Q = (\lambda D)^{-1} \exp \left[\{\alpha - (\lambda/W_-)\}x + \lambda t \right]$$
$$R = (\alpha/\phi)\{\exp \phi(d - x) - 1\},$$
$$\begin{aligned}
D &= (\alpha\gamma/\phi^2 W)\{1 - (1 - \phi d) \exp \phi d\} \\
&\quad + (\delta/\psi^2 W_-)\{1 - (1 - \psi d) \exp \psi d\}.
\end{aligned}$$

Part (ii)

$$\begin{aligned}
g_-^- &= \Sigma G_-^-; \ g_+^- = \Sigma R G_-^- \\
g_-^+ &= \Sigma G_-^+; \ g_+^+ = \Sigma R G_-^+ \\
G_-^- &= \lambda Q F(x_1) \exp \left[\{(\lambda/W_-) - \alpha\}x_1 \right] \\
G_-^+ &= \gamma\lambda Q \exp \{- \lambda x_1/W_+\}
\end{aligned} \Bigg\} \quad . \quad (8.8)$$

From these expressions it is possible to calculate the electron or ion density at any point x in the gap at any time t after the initial electrons are produced. These expressions thus describe the spatio-temporal growth of ionization in the gap. They are of considerable importance in calculating not only formative time lags in overvolted gaps but also the spatio-temporal development of the luminosity produced during the later stages of ionization growth. In Davidson's approximate solution, equation 8.4, $I_-(o, t)$ was of the form

$$A + C \exp \lambda t$$

in which the constant C was not accurately specified. In the important case where there is only a negligible charge distribution between the plates at time zero, Davidson's exact solution for $I_-(o, t)$ (from which $I_-(x, t)$ and $I_+(x, t)$ are immediately calculable) specifies a definite value, say C_0, for the C in the approximate solution and specifies the additional terms which must be added to make the expression exact. These terms have complex λ's, that is, they are oscillations. They are damped relative to the term $C_0 \exp \lambda t$. In practical use, these expressions are not as formidable as they appear. Davidson has given some notes [56] on the practical procedure; and also an alternative form of the exact expression 8.7 suitable for use when the growth is very large even in the first few electron transit times.

For example, during the first electron transit time the expression for $I_-(o, t)$ is

$$I_0 \left\{ \frac{1}{1 + \gamma + \delta/\alpha} + \frac{WW_-}{q_1 - q_2} \left(\frac{\psi_1'\phi_1' \exp q_1 t}{q_1} - \frac{\psi_2'\phi_2' \exp q_2 t}{q_2} \right) \right\} \qquad (8.9)$$

where

$$\phi' = \alpha - q/W$$
$$\psi' = \alpha - q/W_-$$

and q_1, q_2 are the roots of

$$1 + \delta/\psi' + \alpha\gamma/\phi' = 0$$

From these expressions, $I_-(x, t)$ and $I_+(x, t)$ are then given by the formulae

$$\left. \begin{aligned} I_-(x, t) &= I_-(o, t - x/W_-) \exp \alpha x, \\ I_+(x, t) &= \int_x^d \alpha I_-(o, t + x/W_+ - x'/W) \exp \alpha x' \, . \, dx' \end{aligned} \right\} \qquad (8.10)$$

in which $I_-(o, \tau)$ is to be set zero at τ negative. This shows how $I_-(x, t)$ and $I_+(x, t)$ are obtained when $I_-(o, t)$ is known. Thus the practical problem is to find $I_-(o, t)$.

Another paper on the subject is by Auer [10a]. Considering only the case where there is only one of the two secondary processes, γ and δ, he obtains the alternative form of expression 8.7, and uses it to derive an approximate solution for that case. It differs from Davidson's approximate formula 8.4 applied to that case only in that the values of the constants (C_0 and λ) are somewhat altered. If the expression is to be regarded as a smoothed curve of current growth, it would have been better to have retained Davidson's values [56].

Davidson has also given the exact expression for $I_-(o, t)$ in two other forms, valid in the time ranges 0 to d/W and d/W to $2d/W$ respectively. The advantage of these special forms is that in the time ranges in which they hold they usually converge more rapidly than the series given by 8.7, which is valid at all times.

When the ion density becomes sufficient to influence the applied field E the solution of the differential equations becomes excessively complicated because the coefficients α and ω/α (assumed constant in the above treatment), being functions of E, will then be changed by amounts which are difficult to estimate exactly. The mechanism of the ionization is not altered; but with change of field the rate, both spatial and temporal, of the ionization growth can be considerably enhanced by only a slight increase in α. The solution of equations 8.4 or 8.7 for typically practical conditions shows that the spatial and temporal rate of increase of I is already very great even before space-charge distortion occurs and while the field is still uniform. The growing current must eventually cause the gap voltage to fall, either to the value V_g required to maintain a glow discharge, or even lower to the arc value, V_a (see Chapter 4, §§ 4.1 and 4.6.2). However, the temporal rate of growth of the current at this stage is already extremely high (even though the applied field may be falling), so that the time elapsing from the attainment of a current magnitude I at which space charge begins to be significant to the magnitude which produces the eventual fall of voltage is negligibly small. This interval can therefore be neglected in comparison with the much longer time interval during which the current grew (in the uniform field) from the initial magnitude I_0 to that magnitude I. The time t_f at which the electron current at $x = 0$ attains a value $I_-(o, t_f)$ which is given by equation 8.7, and at which the space charge begins to be significant (up to which stage the equations are valid), now becomes the magnitude which must be calculated in order to compare with the observed time or interval up to the instant of voltage collapse.

Equations 8.4, 8.7, and 8.8 show that the time taken for the current in the gap to increase to any given value depends upon the value of I_0. It is thus necessary to consider what values of this initial current are to be used in the analysis in order that the statistical time lag t_s shall be rendered negligible. This may be done by making I_0 sufficiently large.

In order to proceed further with this analysis, it is necessary to relate the current in the gap to the value which, in practice, causes breakdown. The establishment of a clearly visible discharge, for example, could be taken as evidence that complete breakdown of the gap has occurred, so that the current density necessary for the visual detection of the discharge might well be taken to indicate that breakdown has occurred. The value of the particular current density at breakdown is not known, and it is therefore necessary to choose a practical criterion for the application of equations 8.5 or 8.7 for the occurrence of breakdown. At values of $pd \sim 760$ mm.Hg.cm. clearly visible discharges have been observed with currents as low as micro-amps., so that if values of the currents at the cathode $I_-(o, t)$ in the range 10^{-5}–10^{-7} A are to be considered as convenient upper limits for indication of completed breakdown, it is reasonable to assume that this covers a large number of cases of practical interest. Because the rate of current growth becomes so great, the formative time lag calculated does not critically depend on the magnitude of the final current taken to indicate the occurrence of breakdown. Assuming such values of the current $I_-(o, t)$, calculations of the formative time lag can be made for various values of the overvoltage ΔV, on the basis of the operation of various secondary ionization processes ranging from the one extreme case, in which the secondary cathode emission is due only to the incidence of positive ions, to the other extreme case, in which this emission is entirely photo-electric, i.e., for values of the ratio δ/ω ranging from 0 to 1.

Breakdown may also be defined in another way, viz. by the collapse of the gap voltage. The growth formulae may readily be applied to a fully prescribed circuit, and the time to the collapse calculated. This method will be explained in more detail later in § 8.6.4.

Measurements of the growth of pre-breakdown ionization currents in static fields (Chapters IV and V) indicate that the secondary processes operative are, in general, mainly those involving the action at the cathode of photons and positive ions. The influence of these same secondary processes on the temporal growth of ionization currents in uniform fields discussed above may now be examined on the basis of the present analysis. The analysis can also be used to calculate where in the particular gap used, as well as at what time after the application of the field, the space charge appreciably distorts the field and affects α and ω.

Experimental results on impulse breakdown will now be considered.

8.4 Experimental Results on Growth of Ionization

8.4.1 *Data at Low Pressures* ($pd \lesssim 150$ *mm.Hg.cm.*). Early experimental work was carried out by Tank and Graf [257]. Von Gugelburg [99] measured the current flowing through a resistance in series with a discharge gap. Currents between 10^{-11} and 10^{-4} A were observed in H_2, He, A, Kr, N_2, and admixture of Ne and A for values of $pd \lesssim 100$ mm.Hg.cm. with uniform field and also with non-uniform fields. The results were compared with the times calculated on his analysis, and estimates of the relative contribution (δ/ω) of the photo-electric effect to the total secondary emission were made. In Ne and He there appeared to be no perceptible photo-effect, whereas the contribution was 20 per cent in Xe and even greater in H_2. These results are in general agreement with the conclusions reached in § 8.3 above.

Morgan [186, 187, 188] has reported measurement of the growth of current in highly stable, uniform electric fields as a function of the percentage overvoltage $100 \, \Delta V / V_s$ over a wide range of the parameter E/p corresponding to conditions in low-pressure discharges in hydrogen. For low values of E/p (~50 V/cm.mm.Hg) the formative time lags were of the order of μsec. with overvoltages ~1 per cent;

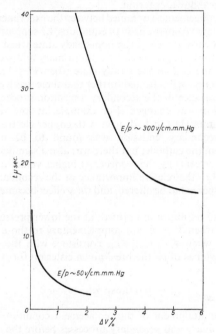

FIG. 8.3. Experimental data on formative times in hydrogen at low pressures obtained at Swansea

while at larger values of E/p (~300 V/cm.mm.Hg) the lag was of the order of m.sec. A typical result is given in Fig. 8.3.

The form of the curve is in general agreement with previous experimental work of Schade [233] and Von Gugelburg. Taking into account the difference of experimental arrangements, there was satisfactory agreement between the results of the different observers at low pressures.

Curves relating the formative time t_f to the percentage overvoltage $100 \, \Delta V / V_s$ were calculated by Morgan. Comparison of such a family of theoretical curves with an experimental family of curves enables the values of the individual coefficients γ and δ/α (comprising ω/α) for the electrode surface actually used in the experiment to be determined. Thus, the experiments can be used to assess the relative significance of the particular secondary process γ or δ/α acting in the neighbourhood of the condition represented by $V = V_s$, i.e., at the static breakdown criterion.

The good agreement so obtained between the experimental data and curves calculated from the growth equations 8.7 supports the conclusion that, in early stages of the non-steady state when $V > V_s$, the ionization growth is produced by both primary and secondary processes, as is the case in the steady state when $V < V_s$. The results illustrated in Fig. 8.3 indicated further that there was a change in the relative importance of the secondary ionization processes when the parameter E/p was changed. For example, at low values of E/p (<50 V/cm.mm.Hg.) in hydrogen with copper electrodes, the predominant secondary emission was found to be photo-electric emission from the cathode, but there was also a significant contribution ($\sim$25 per cent) by the γ effect. At higher values of E/p ($\sim$300 V/cm.mm.Hg.) the relative importance of the secondary ionization processes appeared to be altered, and the γ effect became increasingly important.

These data on ionization growth at the lower pressures with impulse fields when $V > V_s$ are complementary to those obtained in static fields when $V < V_s$, being consistent with the view that at these lower values of pd the breakdown criterion for static uniform fields

$$1 - (\omega/\alpha)(\exp \alpha d - 1) = 0$$

is set by the attainment of the replacement condition through the action of primary and secondary processes before the space charge due to the current significantly distorts the applied field.

A further result of these investigations of time lags at low pressures is that formative time lags $\sim 10^{-6}$ sec. can be obtained with overvoltages as low as 2 per cent. Thus, the assumption that the general mechanism of ionization growth dependent on primary α and secondary processes ω in a uniform field is too slow to give the times $\sim 10^{-6}$ sec. is unfounded. At higher overvoltages the growth times can be even shorter.

8.4.2 *Data at Higher Pressures* ($pd \sim 760$ *mm.Hg.cm.*). For similar numerical computations [170] of formative time lags in air at atmospheric pressure the value of the parameter E/p (V_s/pd_s) was taken as 41·6 V/cm.mm.Hg. and ω/α was calculated from the static spark-ing potential V_s using measured values of α.

The dependence of the shape of the $\{t_f, 100\,\Delta V/V_s\}$ curve on the value of the cathode current $I_-(o, t)$ assumed is illustrated in Fig. 8.4 for the three cases when $\delta/\omega = 1$, 0·5, and 0 respectively. Because

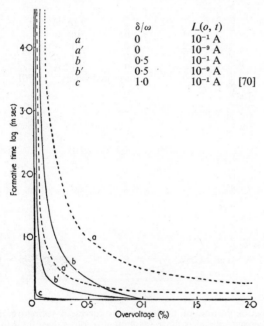

	δ/ω	$I_-(o, t)$
a	0	10^{-1} A
a'	0	10^{-9} A
b	0·5	10^{-1} A
b'	0·5	10^{-9} A
c	1·0	10^{-1} A [70]

Fig. 8.4. Theoretical curves showing the variation of the formative time lag with the percentage over-voltage for various values of δ/ω and $I_-(o, t)$

the value of $I_-(o, t)$ given by equation 8.5 depends on the value as-sumed for the initial photo-electric current I_0, the curves plotted in Fig. 8.4 show also the dependence of the curves on the value of I_0 for a given final value of $I_-(o, t)$. The dependence of the value of t_f on I_0 is more marked, the smaller is δ/ω (i.e., the greater the contribution of secondary electron liberation at the cathode by positive ions to the total cathode emission). These results show that, as at the lower pressures, the action of primary α and secondary ω processes at high pressures can also lead to short formative time lags. For example, when δ/ω is 0·5, t_f is $\sim 10^{-6}$ sec. for a 1-cm. gap with an overvoltage as low as 2 per cent. Further, the time lag calculated was not greatly dependent on the magnitude of the current taken to indicate breakdown.

Measurements of the formative time lags in uniform fields in air

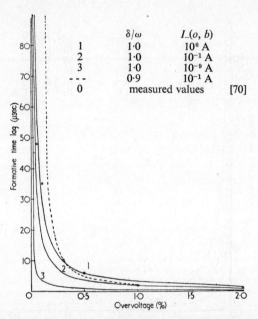

	δ/ω	$I_-(o, b)$
1	1·0	10^6 A
2	1·0	10^{-1} A
3	1·0	10^{-9} A
- - -	0·9	10^{-1} A
0	measured values	[70]

FIG. 8.5. Comparison of the theoretical curves of formative time lag against percentage over-voltage (assuming various values for $I_-(o, t)$ and δ/ω) with the measurements of Fisher and Bederson

have been made by Fisher and Bederson [78], who found long time lags $\sim 10^{-5}$ sec. when $\Delta V/V_s$ was small, but that the times rapidly diminished as $\Delta V/V_s$ increased. They consequently concluded that the breakdown criterion was set by Townsend primary and secondary processes, the latter being almost entirely a photo-effect. Their experimental results are given in Fig. 8.5, together with theoretical curves [70] based on the above analysis of the ionization growth equation 8.5. While the theoretical and experimental curves are of the same form, the agreement is not perfect because the values of the coefficients α and ω/α, and the electron- and ion-drift velocities W_-

and W_+ are not known sufficiently accurately for the conditions of these experiments in air.

Measurements of the current growth in uniform fields using un-degassed brass electrodes in air, in the range 10^{-6} up to 10^{-2} A, and for times between 10 and 100 μsec., have been made by Bandel [12]. In comparing these with theory, his computations were based on Davidson's approximate solution (8.5) of the growth equation, and he assumed that γ was zero.[1] The predicted rate of growth is at first too large, but it must be appreciated that γ may not, in reality, be zero. A rapid current increase is found to occur at about the stage when space charge might be expected to cause failure of the formula. It was concluded that owing to the action of the δ effect the pre-breakdown ionization current was spread over the whole electrode surface; the final discharge observed was, however, filamentary.

More recent time lag data for the development of currents in air in a uniform field gap have been obtained by Aked, Bruce, and Tedford [2], using a standard 1/50 impulse voltage of very high peak value up to 150 kV. For small electrode spacings the data agree with those of Fisher and Bederson for similar distances. At low percentage overvoltages long time lags were observed, which appeared to increase indefinitely as $\Delta V/V_s$ approached zero; t_f decreased rapidly at high overvoltages, being of the order of 1 μsec. at 2 per cent overvoltage, and the authors point out that these values are of the nature and order predicted by theory [69] of the ionization growth given in § 8.3 and illustrated in Fig. 8.4.

Gänger [89] had previously investigated formative time lags in air with potentials up to 50 kV using sphere-to-plane configurations. He found long time lags at low overvoltages from which he concluded that the Townsend mechanism operated and that the β effect might be occurring.

Fisher and his colleagues have also made investigations of the formative time lag for positive-point corona in air [83] and for uniform field breakdown in nitrogen [80], hydrogen [82], oxygen [79], and argon [81] for similar pressure and distance ranges to those used in air. In uniform fields the results obtained for nitrogen and hydrogen were found to be similar to those obtained for air. The time lags decreased rapidly with overvoltage, and there was no observed pressure dependence. In oxygen and argon, on the other hand, the lags were much larger for a given overvoltage than those measured for air, and there was a dependence of time lag on pressure. For the

He overestimated the accuracy of expression 8.5, but in his particular numerical applications the resulting error is not serious.

reasons given above in Chapter VII (non-uniform fields) quantitative assessment of observational data obtained with the non-uniform fields is not easy; a complete theoretical analysis of the temporal growth of ionization in such conditions has not yet been published. Such analysis is, however, required in order to draw fundamental conclusions from experimental data.

From the results in argon it was concluded that the Townsend pre-breakdown ionization-growth mechanism involved a delayed photon δ effect; and such a delayed action had been found in discharges in argon Geiger counters and attributed by Colli [41] to a long-lived molecular state. Further investigations of this effect have been made by Menes [181], who recorded oscillographically the current growth and the light emission after the application of the field. The results are in fair agreement with Colli's data at atmospheric pressures, but deviate at the lower pressures, and further work is needed.

8.5 Later Stages of Ionization Growth; the Spark Diameter

In the previous sections discussion of the ionization growth was carried quantitatively to the stage when the space charge began to be significant. For reasons previously discussed, the current, if permitted continually to increase, will finally distort the field, especially at the cathode where the current density can be high and this will constrict the current. At high pressures the final current density is high, and it is interesting to estimate theoretically the diameter of the spark (*kanal* or streamer) at the stages of the ionization current when the positive-ion field is significant.

It can be shown [143] that for these conditions the continuity equation is

$$\frac{\partial n}{\partial t} = \alpha W_- n + D_- \nabla^2 n - \text{div } n\{W_-(E') - W_-(E)\} \qquad (8.11)$$

where n is the density judged by an observer moving with velocity $W_-(E)$, and where E' is the intensity of the electric field due to the charges on the electrodes and the space charge in the gas, and E is the applied electric field V/d. Space charge in the electron avalanche may be ignored because of the presence of ions, so that $E = E'$. It is seen from equation 8.11 that a quantity $n = n_0 \exp \alpha W_- t$ satisfies

$$\partial n_0 / \partial t = D_- \nabla^2 n_0 \quad . \quad . \quad . \quad (8.12)$$

which is the diffusion equation which the electrons would satisfy if there were no internal generation (by ionization), i.e., if the total number remained n_0. If, therefore, the spatial distribution of n_0 is calculated at any time t by solving equation 8.12, then, since $n = n_0 \exp(\alpha W_- t)$, the spatial distribution of n, the number of electrons, including those internally generated, is the same as that of n_0, i.e., it is also given by equation 8.12.

The cross-section A_1 of the electron avalanche at the anode is approximately $\pi \overline{R^2}$, where $\overline{R^2}$ is the mean square lateral distance in the anode plane of the diffusing electrons. From equation 2.41 of Chapter II,

$$\overline{R^2} = 4D_- t$$

where the gap transit time

$$t = d/W_-$$

Thus

$$A_1 = 4\pi D_- d/W_- = 4\pi d^2 E_1 / V \quad . \quad . \quad . \quad (8.13)$$

where E_1 is the mean energy of the particles.

The high concentration of positive ions originally at the anode will move to the cathode, where the electron concentration is much lower; it is not possible now to neglect the space charge, which will enhance the lateral diffusion in dispersing the cloud. The equation of motion of the positive ions is obtained from 8.11 by putting $\alpha = 0$, giving

$$\frac{\partial n}{\partial t} = D_+ \nabla^2 n - \operatorname{div} n\{W_+(E') - W_+(E)\} \quad . \quad (8.14)$$

But $W_+ = \mu E$, where μ is the positive-ion mobility. Putting $E'' = E' - E$, and

$$\frac{\partial n}{\partial t} = D_+ \nabla^2 n - \operatorname{div} n\mu E'' \quad . \quad . \quad . \quad (8.15)$$

where E'' is the field due to the space charge and its multiple images in the electrodes. Now div $E'' = 4\pi ne$, hence,

$$\frac{\partial n}{\partial t} = D_+ \nabla^2 n - 4\pi\mu en^2 - \mu(E'' \operatorname{grad} n) \quad . \quad (8.16)$$

In over-volted gaps in air at atmospheric pressures, E/p is in the range 40–100 V/cm.mm.Hg.; the mean electron energy $E_1 \sim 4$–10eV; and until the gas becomes greatly heated E_2 for ions is $\sim 0 \cdot 1$eV. Equation 8.13 then gives the ratio A_2/A_1 of the cross-section for electrons and ions as $0 \cdot 025$, thus showing that the diffusion of the ions may be neglected, so that dispersal must be due to their space charge. It may be assumed that the main components of the space charge field E'' and the concentration gradient grad n are both radial and perpendicular to the axial field E. Thus the radius r of a

K

cylindrical surface enclosing a fixed number N of ions per cm. expands at the rate $dr/dt = \mu E' = \mu 2Ne/r$.

Integration gives

$$r_1{}^2 - r_0{}^2 = 4e\mu Nt$$

i.e.,

$$(A_2)_t - (A_2)_0 = 4\pi e\mu Nt = 4\pi ed^2\alpha(\exp \alpha d)/2V \quad . \quad (8.17)$$

It is assumed that the avalanche was generated by the emission of a single electron from the cathode, and if N is given the approximate value $\alpha(\exp \alpha d)/2$, and $(A_2)_0$ the value of A_1 given by equation 8.13, and t set $= d^2/\mu V$, the time for a positive ion to cross the gap, then the area $(A_2)_t$ given by equation 8.17 may be regarded as the area of the resulting cathode hot-spot, and $r_1 = \sqrt{(A_2)_t/\pi}$ its radius.

On the basis of these simplifying assumptions the area A_2 through which the current strikes the anode in a 1-cm. gap in the atmosphere (with $V = 32$ kV, $E_1 = 3\cdot5$ eV, $\alpha = 17$, $A_1 = 1\cdot4 \times 10^{-3}$ cm.^{2}), is given by $(A_2)_t - (A_2)_0 = 1\cdot0 \times 10^{-2}$ cm.^{2}, giving $r_t = 6\cdot0 \times 10^{-2}$ cm. Such comparatively small areas are observed in practice, and high current densities can thus occur at the cathode at which intense local heating and evaporation are produced [143]. Thus a filamentary path can be expected at high pressures: the current is diffuse only at the lower pressures.

8.6 The Breakdown of an Over-volted Gap.

8.6.1 *Basic Considerations.* The formal account, given above, of the growth of ionization produced by primary α and secondary ω processes emphasizes the spatio-temporal character of the growth. At any point along the avalanche path the ionization increases in time at a rate which can be calculated from Davidson's expressions such as 8.7, 8.8, or 8.9 when the coefficients, α and ω, the field E, and the drift velocities W_+ and W_- are all known. This rate is highly sensitive to the value of the overvoltage $V - V_s$, and calculation shows that the expressions predict extremely high rates of ionization growth when $(V - V_s) \sim 10$ per cent of V_s, because of the increase of α and ω with the field. High electron and ion densities are thus attainable in a very short time.

When comparatively short formative times $\sim 10^{-6}$ sec. were first observed [247] they were interpreted as being incompatible with ionization development due to primary and cathode secondary processes in a uniform field. It was considered that the build-up of current produced by the transit of positive ions would involve a large number of transits of the gap by avalanches, and this would require a correspondingly long time ($\sim 10^{-4}$ sec.). The short formative time lags had been observed when considerable overvoltages had been employed and not in cases when $V - V_s$ was small. With considerable overvoltages the expression 8.7 for the growth in fact predicts short times; Fig. 8.4 shows that even when the overvoltage is as low as 2 per cent, short formative times ($\sim 10^{-6}$ sec.) are predicted.

With uniform fields, when $V < V_s$, the initial current I_0 from the cathode is reinforced by emission fI_0 due to secondary processes as the avalanche crosses the gap, where $f < 1$. When $V = V_s$, then $f = 1$, so that the current becomes self-maintained, being capable of continuing by virtue of the fact that secondary processes occurring as the avalanche crosses the gap just maintain the initial electron production when I_0 is zero. With an overvoltage, however, the magnitudes of the coefficients α and ω are enhanced, and the secondary ionization produced while an avalanche crosses the gap will then be more than adequate to replace the initial electrons, that is $f > 1$. Further with an overvolted gap, traversal of the full gap distance d is not necessary to provide the regeneration necessary to give $f = 1$, which is the condition for continued growth when I_0 is finite. Thus, in a highly overvolted gap the current can grow rapidly even when the primary avalanche has only traversed a fraction of the gap distance. In such cases, also, the influence which the movement of the charge in the avalanche has upon the anode potential must be taken into consideration in interpreting data on formative times. This influence, as well as that due to local inductances in the external circuit, can be verified experimentally by using the modern pulse techniques which enable extremely short times $\sim 10^{-9}$ sec. to be recorded.

8.6.2 *Highly Over-volted Gaps.* This special case exhibits some interesting characteristics which must now be considered, because extremely short times t_f have been observed with highly over-volted gaps. For example White [295] has recorded values of t_f of about $2 \cdot 5 \times 10^{-8}$ sec. with a 1-mm. gap between small spheres in air with an overvoltage of about 55 per cent, while Wilson [300] recorded a time of $5 \cdot 10^{-9}$ sec. also with sphere gaps, and Newman [192] observed a time as low as $5 \cdot 10^{-9}$ sec. for sphere gap of 0·257 cm. Important measurements in uniform fields in air at atmospheric pressure have been reported by Fletcher [86], who measured the time t_f elapsing between the application of a rectangular pulse of voltage and the collapse of voltage across the gap. Using overvoltages up to about 300 per cent, Fletcher observed a time as low as $0 \cdot 57 \times 10^{-9}$ sec. for a 1-mm. gap, and results such as this must now be considered. Times of about $5 \cdot 10^{-8}$ sec. found for a 1-mm. sphere gap with considerable overvoltage introduce no fundamental difficulty, because even with an assumed drift speed in these conditions of $3 \cdot 10^7$ cm./ sec. the avalanche transit time is about $5 \cdot 10^{-9}$ sec., and therefore considerably less than the observed formation time; so that a number of avalanche transits can take place in the observed time t_f. On the other hand, with observed times of $0 \cdot 57 \times 10^{-9}$ sec. for a 1-mm. gap, it would follow from the same assumed value of W_- that the avalanche could have crossed only a fraction of the gap before the voltage collapsed; and the collapse of the voltage was what was measured.

8.6.3 *Application of* Kanal *and Streamer Concepts.* A result of this kind might suggest that the Townsend mechanism of ionization growth in the gap cannot account for the breakdown of the gap in these circumstances and that some different and very fast mechanism, such as the *kanal* or streamer, comes into action as soon as the primary avalanche attains a certain size. The formative time lag of the spark would then, on this view, be not much greater than the time taken to attain the critical size ($N_c = \exp \alpha x$) in the time x/W_- (since all growth after this point is reached is postulated to be extremely rapid {see § 5.2}), the time t_f being given by

$$t_f = \frac{\ln N_c}{\alpha W_-}$$

Clearly this procedure is applicable only providing d/W_- is greater than the t_f observed; and in practice high overvoltages must be employed to obtain these very small times. On the basis of such general considerations, Fletcher calculated the value of N_c given by the condition that the field due to the avalanche was approximately equal to V/d, assuming values of α for air given by Sanders [228], the avalanche speed W_- of $0 \cdot 224 \times 10^7 \sqrt{E/1,000}$ cm./sec. and avalanche breadth of 10^{-4} cm. given by Raether [210]. It would follow that t_f should be dependent on $E (= V/d)$ rather than on d, and this Fletcher found to be the case for large overvoltages but not for small. He also found that rigorous calculation of the field due to the critical avalanche size N_c was not necessary, because the value of t_f was altered only by 12 per cent when N_c was increased 10 times. Fletcher found agreement between times calculated in this way and those ($< 10^{-8}$ sec.) measured at the higher overvoltages up to about 300 per cent, but not with the longer times observed at lower overvoltages. This approximate agreement has been taken [178, 215, 133] as indicating that the assumption of streamer action in these conditions was correct. In order to account for extremely short times, Raether suggests that the avalanche in these conditions has attained the critical value $\alpha x = 18$, enhancing the field and consequently the electron mobility, and that enhanced photo-ionization also occurs at this stage to produce very rapid ionization growth both backwards and forwards. This whole process is termed by Raether the *kanal* mechanism, which, it is suggested, becomes effective in air for high values of the spark parameter $pd \gtrsim 1500$ mm.Hg.cm., approximately. He suggested [214] that the *kanal* mechanism manifests itself by the property that the formative time to a voltage collapse can be less than the electron transit time d/W_- (when W_- has a value of about 2×10^7 cm./sec. in the undistorted field V/d), and also by the property of being first an anode-directed streamer and later a cathode-directed streamer, as observed in his cloud-chamber studies.

8.6.4 *Flash Growth Concept of Breakdown—Physical Significance of Short Formative Times*. The following different considerations are, however, relevant to the above interesting view. Consider first the propagation of a given ion density across the gap from the point of view of the rapid spatio-temporal growth of ionization when $V > V_s$, as determined by the expressions 8.7, 8.8, or 8.9 preferably corrected for diffusion. When the electron or ion density in the gas attains a certain value, say N_r, it becomes sufficient to be recorded either as a cloud-chamber track or by observation of luminosity. Consideration of the growth of the avalanche in time, as well as the progression in space, shows that the given concentration N_r will first appear in a position in the gap determined by the overvoltage, and that this concentration will progress at first towards the anode to which the avalanche is travelling. At subsequent times the given ion density N_r will appear at positions in the gap nearer and nearer the cathode, because the density is also growing everywhere in time. Thus, the luminosity, for instance, of the flash growth will appear as a growing column, which may at first be anode-directed (depending on the overvoltage and the length of the gap), and later to be cathode directed [142]. This is just what has been observed [133]. The speed of transit of luminosity is determined by the spatio-temporal growth of ionization in the gap and not by the transit speed of the primary avalanche. The apparent transit speed of the luminous glow, on this view, is in reality a kind of phase velocity: no electrons or ions do, in fact, cross the gap with the high speed with which a luminous streak travels. For low values of avalanche size N, for which field distortion is negligible, expressions such as 8.9 can be used to calculate the stages of the growth outlined above. Higher values of N, say N_r, corresponding to appreciable luminosity and presumably also corresponding to the attainment of appreciable space-charge and field distortion, will modify the transit rates of luminosity calculated in this way. This represents the limit to which at present quantitative treatment of the problem has been carried.

The question of the extremely short time lags of 0.5×10^{-9} sec. observed by Fletcher must now be considered. For high overvoltages a large charge ($e \exp \alpha d$) can grow in the gap even within the avalanche transit time, and the movement of this charge, having an effect similar to that of a current in the external circuit, can lower the

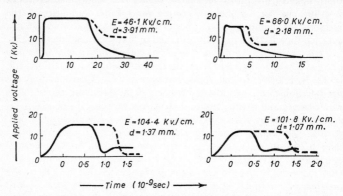

FIG. 8.6. Fletcher's oscillograms of very short time lags and Dickey's calculated times [58]

potential difference across the gap before the charge has actually reached the anode. Thus, with a highly overvolted gap a fast collapse of gap voltage can be recorded *before* the initial avalanche actually reaches the anode; and this collapse can be interpreted as breakdown of the gap occurring in a time less than the avalanche transit time.

If V_t is the potential difference across a gap at time t and V_0 the initial value, then it can be shown [58, 234] that V_t is given by

$$V_t = V_0 - \frac{1}{C} \int_0^t I(t)dt \quad . \quad . \quad . \quad (8.18)$$

where C is the capacity of the gap and $I(t)$ is the spatially averaged current of positive ions and electrons in the gas, the charges not yet having reached the anode, when the current in the external circuit is neglected in these conditions. With considerable overvoltage it can readily be shown that a considerable fall in electrode potential can be produced in times $<10^{-9}$ sec. for a 1-mm. gap, i.e., in general before the avalanche has crossed the gap. Such calculations have been made by Dickey [58], who derived $\{V, t\}$ curves for the conditions of Fletcher's experiments. Some results are given in Fig. 8.6 together with Fletcher's oscillograms. Considering the various uncertainties (e.g., location of the origin on the time axis and the possibility that there was more than one initiating electron), the agreement is considered to be satisfactory. This agreement led Dickey to conclude that the process of ionization in a practically uniform field can account for the required number of electrons in times which, although somewhat longer than the time lags calculated by Fletcher, are still in accordance with his experimental results; and, moreover, to conclude that it is difficult to see how the streamer mechanism can speed up the already extremely rapid ionization process. In other words, extremely short formative times are to be expected on the basis of ionization growth in an undistorted field, provided the overvoltage is adequate. Consequently, a completely different mechanism (fast but unspecified in detail) of ionization development is not required merely to account for the very short formative time observed to occur up to, and including, the collapse of gap-voltage.

8.7 General Conclusions. Further Data Required

Summarizing, it would appear that over the range so far investigated experimentally, present data are consistent with the view that the criterion for breakdown in static uniform fields is set before the space charge of the ionization current becomes large enough significantly to distort the field, the criterion being the Townsend relation. Further, the early stages of temporal growth of current in an overvolted gap have also been shown to take place by a Townsend-type mechanism. However, since the current increases with time the current must eventually distort the field and produce glow or arc conditions, depending on the electrode properties which determine the glow-to-arc transition as the potential falls.

Rigorous quantitative assessment of the cases of overvolted gaps when the observed spark-formative times are about equal to, or at most only a few multiples of, the electron avalanche transit time, requires accurate data on ion- and electron-drift velocities and the ionization coefficients for the conditions obtaining in the experimental measurements of the formative times. There are, however, no sufficiently accurate data at present available on the electron-drift velocities corresponding to these conditions, in spite of the fact that such data are essential for the accurate calculation of ionization growth and gap transit times. When such data are known the times predicted from equation 8.18, where $I(t)$ is obtained from expressions such as 8.9 for the total gap current, can then be compared with those observed over the full range of overvoltages. These equations have general application, and in the cases when they have been applied are found to be in good accord with observation.

Further work is still required on the detailed mechanism for very high values of the parameter pd with static fields, to investigate whether the electric field becomes non-uniform on account of the pre-breakdown current density. Such distortion, although modifying the coefficients α and ω/α, does not in itself constitute an entirely new ionization process. The case of ionization growth by Townsend primary and secondary processes in a field rendered non-uniform by the influence of the space charge of the current is analogous to the case in a field made non-uniform by the geometry of the electrodes, with, however, the difference that the non-uniformity continually changes in time as the current grows.

The full understanding of phenomena of breakdown in uniform electric fields will greatly assist the elucidation of the more complicated phenomena which take place in non-uniform fields. Further work is also required on the elucidation of the final discharge phase of the breakdown process, including the problem of glow-to-arc transition when the breakdown flash acquires the properties of an arc [65, 111, 144]. This phenomenon of transition is greatly dependent on the nature of the cathode surface, and appears also to depend on the current density at the cathode.

CHAPTER IX

Breakdown under High-frequency Alternating Fields

9.1 Introduction

In recent years high-frequency discharges have formed the subject of considerable interest, and important work has been carried out at the Massachusetts Institute of Technology, U.S.A. [15, 22, 24, 204]. Using a method based on the change of resonant frequency of a microwave cavity caused by the presence of an electron concentration, recombination coefficients, mobilities of positive ions, and the atomic cross-section for slow electrons in gases have been measured. An important feature of the method is that data may be obtained when the electrons and gas atoms are practically in thermal equilibrium.

High-frequency discharges have been used as ion sources in nuclear physics [258], for high-frequency torches for welding of refractory materials [40], as detectors of ionizing radiations [23], and as sources for spectrographic analysis. The principles involved are also of interest in connexion with the theory of radio-wave interaction [218, 20, 121]. This monograph concludes, therefore, with a brief account of the principles of electrical breakdown in high-frequency fields [144].

9.2 Types of Breakdown

In a static electric field an electron avalanche is removed from the gas on reaching the anode. If, however, the field is reversed before this occurs, the direction of motion of the electron cloud is reversed, and an avalanche continues to build up due to the general drift velocity in each direction. Thus, under a high-frequency field and with remote electrodes, an electron concentration can build up provided the rate of generation is greater than the rate of loss. Thus, for suitable conditions of oscillation frequency, gap dimensions, and gas pressure, there is no continuous uni-directional drift of electrons to the anode. It is for this reason that the mechanism of high-frequency breakdown is simpler than in the case of static fields; there is no necessity for the action of secondary processes to replace primary electrons lost to the electrodes. When the increase of electron concentration in this way exceeds the loss, electrical breakdown can occur; and the discharge can be produced with values of the electric field very much lower than are required with static electric fields.

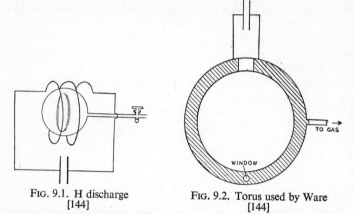

FIG. 9.1. H discharge
[144]

FIG. 9.2. Torus used by Ware
[144]

Such properties make the high-frequency discharge of great interest in the many applications mentioned above.

The oscillatory electric field may be produced in the gas of a discharge tube by internal or external electrodes to which the high-frequency potentials are applied, or by induction from a remote conductor carrying an oscillatory current. Thus, the types of breakdown may be classified according to the mode of excitation: (i) The E, or electrostatic discharge, excited by a field between two conductors as shown in Fig. 9.1. (ii) The H, or ring, discharge where the current forms a closed path in the gas and the glow appears as a luminous ring, illustrated in Fig. 9.2. If ψ is the magnetic flux through an area S of the gas, the exciting field E_r is given by

$$\oint E_r ds = \int_s \psi dS$$

The mechanism of E and H discharges are fundamentally the same, and division into the two types is justified only when the wavelength λ of the high-frequency fields is large compared with the linear dimensions d of the discharge; when $\lambda \simeq d$ the two forms co-exist.

9.2.1 *H Discharge.* The elucidation of the high-frequency breakdown in general is often complicated by the simultaneous occurrence of both the E and H types of discharge, the E discharge being due to the potential difference between the ends of the coil, and the H discharge due to the induction field. In general, the initiation of the discharge is mainly produced by the electrostatic field, and the H discharge appears later with more intense excitation [282, 166, 302]. It follows that the effect of the E field must be eliminated if measurements on H breakdown are to be of fundamental significance. There are no electrodes between which the current and potential difference

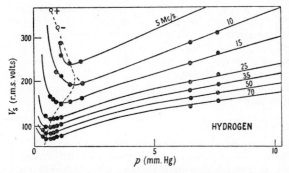

FIG. 9.3. Breakdown in tube A with electrodes oxidized. (Points ● — after de-oxidization) [156]

may be measured, and the length of the discharge path cannot be estimated accurately, and because of such difficulties H breakdown has been comparatively little studied. H breakdown has, nevertheless, been investigated in noble gases, O_2, N_2 and H_2 contained in a glass torus coated on the outside with a layer of copper through which was discharged 1,800 joules from a bank of condensers [291, 45].

9.2.2 *E Discharge.* At low frequencies and high gas pressures the electron cloud must be swept to the electrodes during one half cycle; and the breakdown process is then basically the same as with static fields. When the inter-electrode transit time of the electron is short compared with the period of the field the breakdown potential approximates to that for steady potentials (Chapters IV and V). For higher frequencies of oscillation there is incomplete removal of electrons and ions from the gap during a half period, and this reduction of loss produces progressive lowering of sparking potential V_s; for very high frequencies, or reduced pressure, drift to the electrodes during the half-cycle can be practically eliminated.

Detailed studies of the E discharge have been made for different conditions covering frequencies up to about 100 Mc/s. Recent measurements of V_s in air and hydrogen [156] and in helium [161], using a co-axial electrode system, have been made over the range of frequency from 5 to 70 Mc/s. The variation of V_s with frequency for continuous oscillations for a non-uniform field is given in Fig. 9.3. It is seen that the general shape of the Paschen curve is similar to that obtained with static fields; the ratio E/p diminishes as p increases, and there is steady diminution of V_s as the frequency f increases. When f exceeds 10^9 c/s a state is attained, depending on the ratio f/p, where the period of the field approaches the transit time of the electrons between collisions with the gas molecules. The ionizing efficiency of the field then falls and V_s increases with frequency [104]. Work on pulsed microwave discharges shows that the breakdown field is dependent on the extent to which the gap is irradiated [44, 207]. Prowse and Jasinski [208] have examined breakdown in cavity resonators.

9.3 Influence of Boundaries

For certain values of pressures, frequency, and electrode geometry, the electron cloud can reach the boundaries (whether wall or electrodes), which therefore must exercise some influence on the discharge. In addition to the loss of electrons and ions, there might then be secondary emission of electrons due to the processes discussed above in Chapters III and IV.

Gutton and his collaborators [100] observed under certain conditions two minima in the Paschen curve, and these were shown by Gill and Donaldson [93] to be produced when the drift amplitude of the electrons enabled them to reach the walls or the electrodes.

When the conditions of p, f, and d are such that the electrons do not reach the walls or the electrodes the production of secondary electrons at the boundaries play no part in the discharge, and V_s is then independent of the nature of the electrodes [156]. This is illustrated in Fig. 9.3, in which the points (•) obtained with clean electrodes lay on the full-line curves obtained with oxidized electrodes, from which high secondary emission could be produced; the secondary emission, if it occurred, would be very different for the two conditions of the surface, oxidized or clean (see Chapters III, IV, and VII).

At low pressures ($\sim 10^{-3}$ mm.Hg.), on the other hand, the mean free path of the electrons can be of the same order as, or greater than, the electrode distance or length of the discharge tube; and the chance of a collision between an electron and a gas molecule is then low. In these conditions the work of Gill and von Engel [94, 95] and of Chenot [37] shows that breakdown may be initiated at low potentials ($\lesssim 100$ V) and be independent of the gas pressure provided f is greater than a critical value. This result is interpreted in terms of the emission of electrons from the glass walls of the tube by electrons which have gained sufficient energy (~ 90 V) during a half oscillation of the field. The secondary electrons are in turn accelerated by the field on reversal, and provided the phase relationship is correct, they will arrive at the opposite wall in a half period of the field. The production of electrons is then rapid. Because of the high electron energy, the nature of the gas and small changes of pressure are of little consequence. For each spacing of the walls a cut-off frequency is observed below which it is impossible to obtain breakdown with even very high fields ($\sim 10^2$ V/cm.); above this frequency there is a range in which two values of the breakdown field are obtained [109]. Other work at low pressure has been carried out by von Engel and his collaborators [75, 107].

9.4 The Breakdown Mechanism

The simplest mechanism of breakdown consists of two processes: the generation of electrons (in a pure gas usually by a process of single electron impact with gas molecules) and loss of electrons by diffusion from the ionized region; in certain conditions there is also loss by drift, attachment, or recombination. The necessary conditions for breakdown in this case are that the mean free path l should be small compared with the linear dimensions of the tube (which is itself small compared with the wavelength of the oscillation) and the ionization collision frequency f_i must be less than the collision frequency ν of electrons and gas molecules. In the absence of processes of loss such as attachment and recombination, breakdown occurs when the electron generation by ionization by collision just exceeds electron loss by diffusion and drift. When $f_i < \nu$ the considerations of Chapter II show that the mean energy of the electron cloud will increase under the action of the oscillatory field E; since all directions of motion after scattering are equally probable, the action of the field has little significance in the energy build-up. Holstein [116] has expressed this breakdown criterion for a uniform field by the relation

$$(pd)^2 = \pi^2 E_1/(\alpha/p)(E/p) \quad . \quad . \quad . \quad (9.1)$$

where E_1 is the mean electron energy in electron volts, provided that f is less than the frequency of elastic collisions but greater than the frequency of an inelastic collision. In these conditions the electron-energy distribution is the same as in the static field equal to the r.m.s. value of the high-frequency field [283, 276, 277], and the values of E_1, and the drift velocity W_- measured in experiments with static fields may then be used for h.f. fields. This view has been confirmed [135] in argon at pressures from 3 to 100 mm.Hg. when $f = 3,000$ Mc/s. It has been shown, however, by Margenau [169] that the efficiency of the primary ionization process was not only dependent on E and p but also on the collision frequency f.

The diffusion theory of high-frequency breakdown may be expressed as follows: If q is the volume rate of production of electrons per electron, n_- the electron concentration, and D_- their coefficient of diffusion, the breakdown criterion can be expressed [110] by

$$D_-\nabla^2 n_- + qn_- = 0 \quad . \quad . \quad . \quad . \quad (9.2)$$

When n_- is zero at the electrodes the sparking condition for uniform fields is

$$q/D_-E^2 = \zeta = \pi^2/d^2E^2 \quad . \quad . \quad . \quad (9.3)$$

where ζ is the high-frequency ionizing coefficient which is a function of E/p and f/p. Since

$$q = \alpha\mu E = \alpha W_- \quad . \quad . \quad . \quad . \quad (9.4)$$

where μ_- is the electron mobility and

$$\mu_-/D_- = 1/E_1 \quad . \quad . \quad . \quad . \quad (9.5)$$

it follows that 9.3 is formally the same as 9.1. Values of ζ for air have been calculated from the measured values of V_s in uniform fields with continuous oscillations at about 3,000 Mc/s, and the breakdown conditions for the non-uniform fields between coaxial cylinders have been predicted [110]. The results are in good agreement with the measured values of the fields at breakdown, thus indicating that processes such as recombination, attachment, and secondary emission of electrons from surfaces play a negligible part in the discharge mechanism in air under the particular experimental conditions. The limits within which the diffusion theory of breakdown applies have been fully discussed by Brown and MacDonald [22].

In some earlier investigations of high-frequency breakdown, the assumption was made that the electron acquired ionizing energy over one free path; the energy gained by free electrons, however, in a free path is small compared with the ionization energy, and the breakdown fields predicted were not in accordance with those observed.

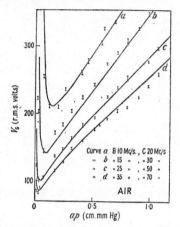

FIG. 9.4. Similarity relationship in air with tube B (curves) and tube C.
(I) [156]

In hydrogen at 1 mm.Hg. the collisional frequency is $\sim 10^9$ collisions/sec. so that the assumption of freely oscillating electrons may be made only if the field frequency is greater than 10^9 c/s. When, however, measurements are made with values of f/p such that $f \sim \nu$, the diffusion theory fails, and the theory of the freely oscillating electron can be expected to hold. Hale [104] has shown that the values of V_s in argon and xenon agreed with those observed, the measurements being made for frequencies from 5 to 50 Mc/s and at gas pressures from 2 to 5×10^{-2} mm.Hg.

The processes involved in the breakdown mechanism of a high-frequency discharge may be investigated from a consideration of the similarity theorem (§ 4.11 and § 7.2.3). When generalized for the high-frequency case the theorem relates the high-frequency breakdown potential V_s of the geometrically similar electrode systems by the expression

$$V_s = \phi(pa, f/p) \quad . \quad . \quad . \quad . \quad (9.6)$$

As in the static case the basis of this principle [169, 156] is that the significant collisional processes are functions of E/p. Excitation or ionization by single-electron impact are processes typical of those dependent on the parameter E/p, where E is the electric field; libera-

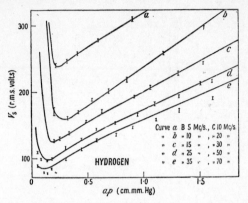

FIG. 9.5. Similarity relationships for hydrogen with tube B (curves) and tube C (I) [156]

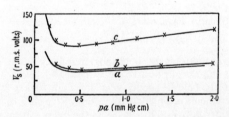

FIG. 9.6. Similarity theorem for pure and impure helium with tubes B ($\times$) and C (curves)

Curve a. C 50 Mc/s, impure helium
Curve b. B 25   ,, ,   ,,
Curve c. B 25   ,, , C 50 Mc/s, pure helium [161]

tion of electrons from electrodes by field emission, volume recombination of ions and electrons, and ionization by collisions of the second kind are processes typical of the group not dependent on E/p. The validity of the similarity theorem for similar high-frequency discharge systems can thus be used to test the nature of the fundamental processes of electron generation and loss which produce breakdown.

In hydrogen and air [156] and in pure helium [160, 161], over a range of pressure from 0·1 to 20 mm. Hg and of frequencies from 5 to 70 Mc/s, the similarity theorem was obeyed, as shown by Figs. 9.4, 9.5, and 9.6. From this it can be concluded that the processes of electron generation and loss were functions of E/p and were probably ionization by single impact and loss by diffusion and drift; at certain values of f and p the effect of drift was negligible. Since the positive ions produced by ionization have only a small drift motion, these results show that space charge plays a negligible part in the breakdown.

The case of helium is interesting. In the presence of traces of impurity ($\sim 0·001$ per cent) the similarity theorem did not hold [160, 161], but when the impurity was removed the theorem was satisfied. This showed that in the presence of impurity a process of either generation or loss occurred which was not dependent on E/p. Such a process is that involving collisions of the second kind (§ 3.4); the reaction being expressed by the relation

$$He_m + H_2 \longrightarrow He + H_2^+ + \varepsilon$$

In this way the similarity theorem has been used as a tool to investigate fundamental processes of the breakdown mechanism in high-frequency fields.

L

Bibliography

TEXTBOOKS

Conduction of Electricity through Gases. 2nd edn. J. J. Thomson, 1906. 3rd edn. Vols. I and II. J. J. and G. P. Thomson, 1936. (Cambridge: University Press.)

Electricity in Gases, J. S. Townsend (Oxford: Clarendon Press), 1915.

Handbuch der Experimental Physik, 13, 3 (Leipzig: Springer), 1929.

Les Phénomènes Élémentaires de la décharge électrique dans les gaz, M. Laporte (Paris), 1933.

Elektrische Gasentladungen, A. H. von Engel and M. Steenbeck (Berlin: Springer), Bd I, 1932, Bd II, 1934.

Mobility of Positive Ions, A. M. Tyndall (Cambridge: University Press), 1938.

Fundamental Processes of Electrical Discharges in Gases, L. B. Loeb (New York: Wiley), 1939.

Behaviour of Slow Electrons in Gases, R. Healey and J. W. Reed (Sydney: Amalgamated Wireless), 1941.

Gaseous Conductors, J. D. Cobine (New York: McGraw-Hill), 1941.

Electrons in Gases, J. S. Townsend (London: Hutchinson), 1947.

Theory of Atomic Collisions, N. F. Mott and H. S. W. Massey (Oxford: Clarendon Press), 1949.

Negative Ions, H. S. W. Massey (Cambridge: University Press), 1950.

Electronic and Ionic Impact Phenomena, H. S. W. Massey and E. H. S. Burhop (Oxford: Clarendon Press), 1952.

Electrical Breakdown of Gases, J. M. Meek and J. D. Craggs (Oxford: Clarendon Press), 1953.

Dielectrics and Waves, A. von Hippel (London: Chapman and Hall), 1954.

Ionized Gases, A. von Engel (Oxford: Clarendon Press), 1956.

Handbuch der Physik, Vols. 21 and 22 (Heidelberg: Springer), 1956.

REVIEWS

'Electrical Discharges in Gases, Pts. 1 and 2', K. T. Compton and I. Langmuir, *Review of Modern Physics,* American Physical Society. 2, 132 (1930) and 3, 191 (1931).

'Mechanism of Electrical Discharges in Gases of Low Pressures', M. J. Druyvesteyn and F. M. Penning, *Review of Modern Physics,* American Physical Society, 12, 87, 1940.

'Electrical Discharges in Gases and their Applications', V. J. Francis and H. G. Jenkins, *Report on Progress in Physics*, Physical Society, London. VII, 230, 1940.

'Electrical Discharges', F. Llewellyn Jones, *Report on Progress in Physics*, Physical Society, London. XVI, 216, 1953.

MONOGRAPHS

Conduction of Electricity through Gases, K. G. Emeleus, 3rd edn. (London: Methuen), 1951.

Collision Processes in Gases, F. L. Arnot, 4th edn. (London: Methuen), 1950.

Atomic Spectra, R. C. Johnson, 2nd edn. (London: Methuen), 1952.

Wave Mechanics, H. T. Flint, 8th edn. (London: Methuen), 1953.

References

1. ABDELNABI, I., and MASSEY, H. S. W. 1953, *Proc. Phys. Soc.* A, **66,**, 288.
2. AKED, A., BRUCE, F. M., and TEDFORD, D. J. 1955, *Brit. J. appl. Phys.* **6,** 233.
3. ALLIBONE, T. E. 1938, *J. Inst. Elect. Engrs.* **82,** 513.
4. ALLIBONE, T. E., and MEEK, J. M. 1938, *Proc. Roy. Soc.* A, **166,** 97.
5. ———— and MEEK, J. M. 1937, *Nature*, **140,** 804.
6. ———— HOWLEY, G., and PERRY, F. R. 1934, *J. Inst. Elect. Engrs.* **75,** 670
7. ———— and SCHONLAND, B. J. F. 1934, *Nature*, **134,** 736.
8. ALLIS, W. P., and ALLEN, H. W. 1937, *Phys. Rev.* **52,** 703.
9. APPLETON, E. V., and CHAPMAN, S. 1937, *Proc. Roy. Soc.* A, **158,** 1.
10. ARNOT, F. L. 1950, *Collision Processes in Gases*, Ch. VI (London: Methuen).
10a. AUER, P. L. 1955, *Phys. Rev.* **98,** 320.
11. AYRES, T. L. R. 1923, *Phil. Mag.* **45,** 353.
12. BANDEL, H. W. 1954, *Phys. Rev.* **95,** 1117.
13. BARTHOLOMEYCZYK, W. 1940, *Z. Phys.* **116,** 235.
14. BEECK, O. 1930, *Ann. Phys.* **6,** 1001.
15. BIONDI, M. A., and BROWN, S. C. 1949, *Phys. Rev.* **76,** 1697.
16. ———— and BROWN, S. C. 1949, *Phys. Rev.* **75,** 1700.
17. BLEAKNEY, W., and SMITH, P. T. 1936, *Phys. Rev.* **49,** 402.
18. BOULIND, H. F. 1934, *Phil. Mag.* **18,** 909.
19. BOULLOUD, A. 1951, *C.R. Acad. Sci.* (Paris), **232,** 958.
20. BOWLS, W. E. 1938, *Phys. Rev.* **53,** 297.
21. BOYLE, W. S., and KISLIUK, P. 1955, *Phys. Rev.* **97,** 255.
22. BROWN, S. C., and MACDONALD, A. D. 1949, *Phys. Rev.* **76,** 1692.
23. ———— and MCCARTHY, J. J. 1948, *Rev. sci. Instrum.* **19,** 851.
24. ———— and ROSE, D. J. 1952, *J. appl. Phys.* (New York), **23,** 711 and 719.
25. BRUCE, C. E. R. 1944, *Proc. Roy. Soc.* A, **183,** 228.
26. ———— 1955, *J. Inst. Elect. Engrs.* **1,** 805.
27. ———— 1941, *Nature*, **147,** 805.
28. ———— 1948, *Nature*, **161,** 521.
29. ———— and GOLDE, R. H. 1942, *J. Inst. Elect. Engrs.* **88,** 487.
30. BRUCE, F. M. 1947, *J. Inst. Elect. Engrs.* **94** (II), 138.
31. ———— 1951, *J. Inst. Radio Engrs.* **11,** 121.
32. ———— 1954, *Endeavour*, **13,** 61.
33. DE BRUYNE, N. A. 1928, *Proc. Roy. Soc.* A, **120,** 423.

34. BURHOP, 1953, *Report of Conference on the Physics of Ionized Gases* (London).

35. CAHN, J. H. 1949, *Phys. Rev.* **75**, 293.

36. CARR, W. R. 1903, *Phil. Trans.* A, **201**, 403.

37. CHENOT, M. 1948, *Ann. Phys.* (Paris), **3**, 277.

38. COBAS, A., and LAMB, W. E. 1944, *Phys. Rev.* **65**, 327.

39. COBINE, J. D., and EASTON, E. C. 1943, *J. appl. Phys.* (New York), **14**, 321.

40. COBINE, J. D., and WILBUR, D. A. 1951, *J. appl. Phys.* (New York), **22**, 835.

41. COLLI, L. 1954, *Phys. Rev.* **95**, 892.

42. —— and FACCHINI, V. 1954, *Phys. Rev.* **96**, 1.

43. COMPTON, K. T., and VAN VOORHIS, C. C. 1926, *Phys. Rev.* **27**, 724.

44. COOPER, R. 1947, *J. Inst. Elect. Engrs.* Pt. III, **94**, 315.

45. COUSINS, S. W., and WARE, A. A. 1951, *Proc. Phys. Soc.* B, **64**, 159.

46. CRANBERG, L. 1952, *J. appl. Phys.* (New York), **23**, 327.

47. CRAVATH, A. M. 1930, *Phys. Rev.* **36**, 248.

48. —— 1935, *Phys. Rev.* **47**, 254A.

49. CROMPTON, R. W., DUTTON, J., and HAYDON, S. C. 1956, *Proc. Phys. Soc.* B, **69**, 2.

50. —— DUTTON, J., and HAYDON, S. C. 1955, *Appl. Sci. Res.* B (The Hague), **5**, 43.

51. —— DUTTON, J., and HAYDON, S. C. 1955, *Nature*, **176**, 1079.

52. CROWE, R. W., BRAGG, J. K., and THOMAS, V. G. 1954, *Phys. Rev.* **96**, 10.

53. CURTIS, J. P. 1954, *Phys. Rev.* **94**, 908.

54. DAVIDSON, P. M. 1954, *Proc. Phys. Soc.* B, **67**, 159.

55. —— 1953, *Brit. J. appl. Phys.* **4**, 170.

56. —— 1955, *Phys. Rev.* **99**, 1072. 1956, *ibid.* **103**, 1897.

57. DAVYDOV, B. 1935, *Phys. Zeits. Sowjet*, **8**, 59.

58. DICKEY, F. R. 1952, *J. appl. Phys.* **23**, 1336 (New York).

59. DIDLAUKIS, M. 1933, *Z. Phys.* **82**, 709; and 1932, **74**, 624.

60. DOLAN, W. W., and DYKE, W. P. 1954, *Phys. Rev.* **95** 327.

61. DYKE, W. P., and TROLAN, J. K. 1953, *Phys. Rev.* **91**, 1054.

62. DRUYVESTEYN, M. J. 1930, *Physica*, **10**, 61.

63. —— 1934, *Physica*, **1**, 1003.

64. —— 1936, *Physica*, **3**, 65.

65. —— and PENNING, F. M. 1940, *Rev. Mod. Phys.* (New York), **12**, 87.

66. —— and PENNING, F. M. 1940, *Rev. Mod. Phys.* **12**, 119.

67. DUSHMAN, S. 1923, *Phys. Rev.* **21**, 623.

68. DUTTON, J., HAYDON, S. C., and LLEWELLYN JONES, F. 1952, *Proc. Roy. Soc.* A, **213**, 203.

69. —— HAYDON, S. C., and LLEWELLYN JONES, F. 1953, *Proc. Roy. Soc.* A, **218**, 206 (with Math. App. by Davidson, P. M.).

70. —— HAYDON, S. C., and LLEWELLYN JONES, F. 1953, *Brit. J. appl. Phys.* **4**, 170.

71. DYKE, W. P., and TROLAN, J. K. 1953, *Phys. Rev.* **89**, 799.

72. EARHART, R. F. 1901, *Phil. Mag.* **6** (i), 147.

73. ECKER, G., and EMELEUS, K. G. 1954, *Proc. Phys. Soc.* B, **67**, 546.
74. EINSTEIN, A. 1905, *Ann. Phys.* **17**, 132.
75. VON ENGEL, A. H., and FRANCIS, C. 1950, *Proc. Phys. Soc.* B, **63**, 825.
76. ENGSTROM, R. W., and HUXFORD, W. S. 1940, *Phys. Rev.* **58**, 67.
77. FISHER, L. H. 1943, *Phys. Rev.* **64**, 187.
78.   and BEDERSON, B. 1951, *Phys. Rev.* **81**, 109.
79.   and KACHIKAS, G. A. 1950, *Phys. Rev.* **79**, 232.
80.   and KACHIKAS, G. A. 1952, *Phys. Rev.* **88**, 878.
81.   and KACHIKAS, G. A. 1953, *Phys. Rev.* **91**, 775.
82.   and LESSIN, I. 1954, *Phys. Rev.* **93**, 649.
83.   and MENES, M. 1951, *Phys. Rev.* **86**, 134.
84.   and MENES, M. 1954, *Phys. Rev.* **94**, 1.
85.   and WEISSLER, G. L. 1944, *Phys. Rev.* **66**, 95.
86. FLETCHER, R. C. 1949, *Phys. Rev.* **76**, 1501.
87. FOWLER, R. H., and NORDHEIM, L. W. 1928, *Proc. Roy. Soc.* A, **119**, 173.
88. FUCHS, W. 1950, *Arch. Elektrotech.* **40**, 1 and 16.
89. GÄNGER, B. 1949, *Arch. Elektrotech.* **39**, 508.
90. GERMER, L. H., and HAWORTH, F. E. 1949, *J. appl. Phys.* **20**, 1085.
91.   and HAWORTH, F. E. 1948, *Phys. Rev.* **73**, 1121.
92.   and HAWORTH, F. E. 1948, *Phys. Rev.* **73**, 1122.
93. GILL, E. W. B., and DONALDSON, R. H. 1931, *Phil. Mag.* **12**, 719.
94.   and VON ENGEL, H. 1948, *Proc. Roy. Soc.* A, **192**, 446.
95.   and VON ENGEL, H. 1949, *Proc. Roy. Soc.* A, **197**, 112.
96. VAN DE GRAAF, R. J., TRUMP, J. G., and BEUCHNER. 1946, *Rep. Prog. Phys.* (London), **11**, 1.
97. GREINER, A. 1933, *Z. Phys.* **81**, 543.
98. GRIGOROVICI, R. 1939, *Z. Phys.* **111**, 596.
99. VON GUGELBERG, H. L. 1947, *Helv. phys. Acta.* **20**, 250 and 307.
100. GUTTON, C., and GUTTON, H. 1928, *C.R. Acad. Sci.* (Paris), **186**, 303.
101. HAGSTRUM, H. D. 1953, *Phys. Rev.* **89**, 244.
102.   1953, *Phys. Rev.* **91**, 543.
103.   1954, *Phys. Rev.* **96**, 325 and 336.
104. HALE, D. H. 1948, *Phys. Rev.* **73**, 1046.
105. HALLWACHS, W. 1888, *Ann. Phys.* **33**, 301.
106. HANLE, W. 1929, *Z. Phys.* **61**, 94.
107. HARRIES, W. H., and VON ENGEL, A. H. 1951, *Proc. Phys. Soc.* B, **64**, 915.
108. HASTED, J. B. 1953, *Report on Conference on Ionization Physics* (London: Royal Society).
109. HATCH, A. J., and WILLIAMS, H. B. 1951, *Conference on Gaseous Electronics* (New York).
110. HERLIN, M. R., and BROWN, S. C. 1948, *Phys. Rev.* **74**, 291, 902.
111. VON HIPPEL, A. 1954, *Dielectrics and Waves* (New York: J. Wiley).
112. VON HIPPEL, A., and FRANCK, J. 1929, *Z. Phys.* **57**, 696.
113. HOBBS. 1905, *Phil. Mag.* (6) **10**, 617.
114. HOCHBERG, B., and SANDBERG, E. 1942, *J. Tech. Phys.* (U.S.S.R.), **12**, 65.
115. HOLM, R. 1924, *Z. Phys.* **25**, 497.

116. HOLSTEIN, T. 1946, *Phys. Rev.* **69,** 50.
116a. HORNBECK, J. A. 1951, *Phys. Rev.* **83,** 375.
117. HORTON, F., and MILLEST, D. M. 1946, *Proc. Roy. Soc.* A, **185,** 381.
118. HOUTERMANS, F. G. 1927, *Z. Phys.* **41,** 619.
119. HOWELL, A. H. 1939, *Trans. Amer. Inst. Elect. Engrs.* **58,** 193.
120. HUXLEY, L. G. H. 1950, *Proc. Roy. Soc.* A, **200,** 486.
121.   FOSTER, H. G., and NEWTON, C. C. 1948, *Proc. Phys. Soc.* **61,** 134.
122.   and ZAAZOU, A. 1949, *Proc. Roy. Soc.* A, **196,** 402.
123. JACOB, L. 1934, *High Voltage Physics* (London: Methuen).
124. JENKINS, R. O. 1943, *Rep. Prog. Phys.* **9,** 177.
125. JOHNSON, G. W. 1948, *Phys. Rev.* **73,** 284.
126. JONES, T. J. 1936, *Thermionic Emission* (London: Methuen).
127. KAPITZA, L. 1923, *Phil. Mag.* **45,** 989.
128. KERNER, K., and RAETHER, H. 1954, *Z. angew. Phys.* **6,** 212.
129. KOMELKOV, V. 1947, *Dok. Akad. Nauk.* (U.S.S.R.), **68,** 57.
130. KINSLEY, C. 1905, *Phil. Mag.* (6), **9,** 692.
131. KISLIUK, P. 1954, *J. appl. Phys.* (New York), **25,** 897.
132. KOHRMANN, W. 1955, *Z. angew. Phys.* **7,** 183.
133.   and RAETHER, H. 1954, *Naturwissenschaften,* **17,** 400.
134.   and RAETHER, H. 1953, *Z. angew. Phys.* **6,** 211.
135. KRASIK, S., ALPERT, D., and MCCOUBREY, A. O. 1949, *Phys. Rev.* **76,** 722.
136. KRUITHOFF, A. A. 1940, *Physica,* **7,** 530.
137.   and PENNING, F. M. 1936, *Physica,* **3,** 515.
138. VON LAUE, M. 1925, *Ann. Phys.* (Leipzig), **76,** 261.
139. LEES, J. H. 1932, *Proc. Roy. Soc.* A, **137,** 173.
140. LLEWELLYN JONES, F. 1949, *Proc. Phys. Soc.* B, **62,** 366.
141.   1953, *Proc. Inst. Elect. Engrs.* **100,** (1), 169.
142.   1954, *Brit. J. appl. Phys.* **5,** 49.
143.   1950, *Brit. J. appl. Phys.* **1,** 60.
144.   1953, *Rep. Prog. Phys.* (London), **16,** 216. Electrical Discharges.
145.   1931, *Phil. Mag.* **11,** 163.
146.   1933, *Phil. Mag.* **15,** 958.
147.   1939, *Phil. Mag.* **28,** 192 and 328.
148.   1956, *Handbuch d. Phys.* **22.** Ionisation Growth and Breakdown.
149.   1954, *Vacuum* (London), **3,** 116.
150.   and DAVIES, D. E. 1951, *Proc. Phys. Soc.* B, **64,** 397.
151.   and DAVIES, D. E. 1951, *Proc. Phys. Soc.* B, **64,** 519.
152.   and GALLOWAY, W. R. 1938, *Proc. Phys. Soc.* **50,** 207.
153.   and HENDERSON, J. P. 1939, *Phil. Mag.* **28,** 185.
154.   and MORGAN, C. G. 1953, *Proc. Roy. Soc.* A, **218,** 88.
155.   and MORGAN, C. G. 1951, *Phys. Rev.* **82,** 970.
156.   and MORGAN, G. D. 1951, *Proc. Phys. Soc.* B, **64,** 560, 574.
157.   and PARKER, A. B. 1952, *Proc. Roy. Soc.* A, **213,** 185.
158.   and PARKER, A. B. 1950, *Nature,* **165,** 960.
159.   and DE LA PERELLE, E. T. 1953, *Proc. Roy. Soc.* A, **216,** 267.
160.   and WILLIAMS, G. C. 1953, *Proc. Phys. Soc.* B, **66,** 345.
161.   and WILLIAMS, G. C. 1953, *Proc. Phys. Soc.* B, **66,** 17.

162. LOEB, L. B. 1928, *J. Franklin Inst.* **205**, 305.
163.   1930, *J. Franklin Inst.* **210**, 15.
164.   1939, *Fundamental Processes in Electrical Discharges in Gases*, p. 371 (New York: John Wiley).
165.   and MEEK, J. M. 1941, *Mechanism of the Electric Spark*, Ch. I (California: Stanford University Press).
166. MACKINNON, K. A. 1929, *Phil. Mag.* **8**, 605.
167. MCCALLUM, S. P., and KLATZOW, L. 1931, *Phil. Mag.* **17**, 291.
168. MCEACHRON, K. B. 1939, *J. Franklin Inst.* **227**, 149.
169. MARGENAU, M. H. 1948, *Phys. Rev.* **73**, 297–328.
170. MASCH, K. 1932, *Arch. Elektrotech.* **26**, 589.
171. MASSEY, H. S. W. 1950, *Negative Ions* (Cambridge: University Press).
172.   1953, *Report of Conference on the Physics of Ionized Gases* (London: Royal Society).
173.   and BURHOP, E. H. S. 1952, *Electronic and Ionic Impact Phenomena* (Oxford: Clarendon Press).
174.   and BURHOP, E. H. S. 1952, *Electronic and Ionic Impact Phenomena* Ch. 2 (Oxford: Clarendon Press).
175.   and BURHOP, E. H. S. 1952, *Electronic and Ionic Impact Phenomena*, p. 632 (Oxford: Clarendon Press).
176.   and BURHOP, E. H. S. 1952, *Electronic and Ionic Impact Phenomena*, Ch. 9 (Oxford: Clarendon Press).
177. MEEK, J. M. 1940, *Phys. Rev.* **57**, 722.
178.   and CRAGGS, J. D. 1953, *Electrical Breakdown of Gases* (Oxford: Clarendon Press).
179.   and CRAGGS, J. D. 1953, *Electrical Breakdown of Gases*, Ch. VI, p. 279 (Oxford: Clarendon Press).
180.   and CRAGGS, J. D. 1953, *Electrical Breakdown of Gases*, Ch. III (Oxford: Clarendon Press).
181. MENES, M. 1954, *Gaseous Electronics Conference* (New York).
182. MICHELS, W. C. 1930, *Phys. Rev.* **36**, 1363.
183. MILLER, C. G., and LOEB, L. B. *Phys. Rev.* **73**, 84.
184. MILLIKAN, R. A. 1916, *Phys. Rev.* **7**, 355.
185. MOLNAR, J. P. 1951, *Phys. Rev.* **83**, 933 and 940.
186. MORGAN, C. G. 1953, *Report of Conference on the Physics of Ionized Gases* (London).
187.   1954, *Report of Conference on the Physics of Ionized Gases* (Birmingham).
188.   1955, *Appl. Sci. Res.* B, **5**, 18 (The Hague). 1956, *Phys. Rev.* **104**, 566.
189.   and HARCOMBE, D. 1953, *Proc. Phys. Soc.* B, **66**, 665.
190. MORSE, P. M., ALLIS, W. P., and LAMAR, E. S. 1935, *Phys. Rev.* **48**, 412.
191. MORTON, P. L. 1946, *Phys. Rev.* **70**, 358.
192. NEWMAN, M. 1937, *Phys. Rev.* **52**, 652.
193. NORDHEIM, L. W. 1928, *Proc. Roy. Soc.* A, **121**, 626.
194.   1929, *Phys. Z.* **30**, 177.

195. NORRINDER, H., and SALKA, O. 1951, *Ask. Fysik*, **3**, 347.
196.   and SALKA, O. 1952, *Ask. Fysik*, **5**, 493.
197. OLIPHANT, M. L. E. 1929, *Proc. Roy. Soc.* A, **124**, 228.
198.   and MOON, P. B. 1930, *Proc. Roy. Soc.* A, **127**, 388.
199. PAAVOLA, M. 1929, *Arch. Electrotech.* **22**, 443.
200. PAETOW, H. 1939, *Z. Phys.* **110**, 770.
201. PASCHEN, F. 1889, *Weid. Ann.* **37**, 69.
202. PENNING, F. M. 1931, *Proc. Roy. Acad. Amst.* **34**, 1305.
203.   1931, *Phil. Mag.* **11**, 961.
204. PHELPS, A. V., FUDINGSLAND, O. T., and BROWN, S. C. 1951, *Phys. Rev.* **84**, 559.
205. PIERCE, E. T. 1955, *Quart. J. Roy. Meteorol. Soc.* **81**, 211.
206. POSIN, D. Q. 1936, *Phys. Rev.* **50**, 650.
207.   1948, *Phys. Rev.* **73**, 496.
208. PROWSE, W. A., and JASINSKI, W. 1951, *Proc. Inst. Elect. Engrs.* **98**, (iv), 101.
209. RAETHER, H. 1936, *Phys. Z.* **15**, 560.
210.   1937, *Z. Phys.* **107**, 91.
211.   1938, *Z. Phys.* **110**, 611.
212.   1939, *Z. Phys.* **112**, 464.
213.   1941, *Z. Phys.* **117**, 375 and 524.
214.   1953, *Z. angew. Phys.* **6**, 211.
215.   1955, *Z. angew. Phys.* **7**, 50.
216.   1942, *Elektrotech. Z*, **63**, 301.
217. RAMSAUER, C. 1923, *Ann. Phys.* **72**, 345.
218. RATCLIFFE, J. A., and SHAW, I. J. 1948, *Proc. Roy. Soc.* A, **193**, 311.
219. RICHARDSON, O. W. 1902, *Proc. Cambridge Phil. Soc.* **11**, 286.
220.   1914, *Phil. Mag.* **28**, 633.
221. ROGOWSKI, W. 1928, *Arch. Elektrotech.* **20**, 99.
222.   1926, *Arch. Elektrotech.* **16**, 496.
223. ROSE, D. J. 1954, *Conference on Gaseous Electronics* (New York).
224. DE LA RUE, W., and MULLER, H. W. 1880, *Phil. Trans. Roy. Soc.* **171**, 109.
225. SAHA, M. N. 1920, *Phil. Mag.* **40**, 472, 809.
226.   1921, *Proc. Roy. Soc.* A, **99**, 135.
227. SANDERS, F. H. 1932, *Phys. Rev.* **41**, 667.
228.   1933, *Phys. Rev.* **44**, 1020.
229. SAYERS, J. 1938, *Proc. Roy. Soc.* A, **169**, 83.
230.   1950, *Proc. conf. Ionos, Phys. State Coll.* (Pennsylvania).
231.   1943, *Rep. Prog. Phys.* **9**, 52.
232.   1947, *Nature*, **159**, 117.
233. SCHADE, R. 1937, *Z. Phys.* **104**, 487.
234. SCHMIDT, K. J. 1954, *Z. Phys.* **139**, 251.
235. SCHNEIDER, E. G. 1940, *J. Opt. Soc. Amer.* **30**, 128.
236. SCHNITGER, H. 1936, *Z. Phys.* **102**, 163.
237. SCHONLAND, B. F. J. 1938, *Proc. Roy. Soc.* A, **164**, 132.
238.   1953, *Proc. Roy. Soc.* A, **220**, 25.

239. SCHONLAND, B. F. J., 1937, *Phil. Mag.* **23**, 503.

240.   MALAN, D. J., and COLLENS, H. 1935, *Proc. Roy. Soc.* A, **152**, 595.

241.   HODGES, D. B., and COLLENS, H. 1938, *Proc. Roy. Soc.* A, **166**, 56.

242. SCHOTTKY, W. 1923, *Z. Phys.* **14**, 63.

243.   1924, *Phys. Z.* **25**, 342.

244.   1924, *Phys. Z.* **25**, 635.

245. SCHUMANN, W. O. 1923, *Elektrische Durchbruch feldstarke von Gasen* (Berlin: Springer).

246. SEEGER, K. 1953, *Z. Phys.* **135**, 152.

247. SEELIGER, R., and MIERDEL, G. 1929, Handb. d. Experphysik. **13**, (3), § 1.

248. SHENSTONE, A. G. 1931, *Phys. Rev.* **38**, 873.

249. SKILLING, H. H. 1939, *Trans. Amer. Inst. Elect. Engrs.* **58**, 161.

250.   and BRENNER, W. C. 1941, *Trans. Amer. Inst. Elect. Engrs.* **60**, 112.

251. SMIT, J. A. 1936, *Physica*, **3**, 543.

252. SOMERVILLE, J. M. 1952, *Proc. Phys. Soc.* B, **65**, 620.

253. STEENBECK, M. 1930, *Wiss. Veroff. Siemens-Konz.* **9**, 42.

254. STEPHENSON, J. S. 1933, *J. Inst. Elect. Engrs.* **73**, 69.

255. SUTTON, R. M., and MOUZON, J. C. 1930, *Phys. Rev.* **35**, 694.

256.   and MOUZON, J. C. 1931, *Phys. Rev.* **37**, 379.

257. TANK, F., and GRAF, K. 1929, *Helv. phys. Acta.* **2**, 33.

258. THONEMANN, P. C., MOFFAT, J., ROAF, D., and SANDERS, J. H. 1948, *Proc. Phys. Soc.* **61**, 483.

259. THOMPSON, J. J. 1924, *Phil. Mag.* **47**, 337.

260.   1899, *Proc. Cambridge Phil. Soc.* **10**, 74.

261.   1906, 2nd edition, *Conduction of Electricity through Gases* (Cambridge: University Press).

262.   and THOMPSON, G. P. 3rd edition, Vol. 1, 1928, Vol. 2, 1933, *Conduction of electricity through Gases* (Cambridge: University Press).

263. TOWNSEND, J. S. 1925, *Motions of Electrons in Gases* (Oxford: Clarendon Press).

264.   1915, *Electricity in Gases* (Oxford: Clarendon Press).

265.   1915, *Electricity in Gases*, p. 319 (Oxford: Clarendon Press).

266.   1915, *Electricity in Gases*, Ch. VIII (Oxford: Clarendon Press).

267.   1915, *Electricity in Gases*, Ch. IX (Oxford: Clarendon Press).

268.   1915, *Electricity in Gases*, Ch. XI (Oxford: Clarendon Press).

269.   1910, *The Theory of Ionisation of Gases by Collision* (London: Constable).

270.   1910, *The Theory of Ionisation of Gases by Collision*, pp. 24–6 (London: Constable).

271.   1910, *The Theory of Ionisation of Gases by Collision*, p. 42 (London: Constable).

272.   1910, *The Theory of Ionisation of Gases by Collision*, pp. 56–8 (London: Constable).

273.   1910, *The Theory of Ionisation of Gases by Collision*, p. 61 (London: Constable).

274. TOWNSEND, J. S. 1910, *The Theory of Ionisation of Gases by Collision*, Ch. IV (London: Constable).
275. 1930, *Phil. Mag.* **9**, 1145.
276. 1932, *Phil. Mag.* **13**, 745.
277. 1933, *Phil. Mag.* **16**, 720.
278. 1936, *Phil. Mag.* **22**, 145.
279. 1923, *Phil. Mag.* **45**, 444.
280. 1928, *Comptes Rendus*, **186**, 55.
281. and BAILEY, V. A. 1922, *Phil. Mag.* **43**, 593.
282. and DONALDSON, R. H. 1928, *Phil. Mag.* **5**, 178.
283. and LLEWELLYN JONES, F. 1931, *Phil. Mag.* **11**, 679 and **12**, 815.
284. and MCCALLUM, S. P. 1928, *Phil. Mag.* **6**, 857.
285. and MCCALLUM, S. P. 1934, *Phil. Mag.* **17**, 678.
286. TRUMP, J. G., CLOUD, R. W., MANN, J. G., and HANSON, E. P. 1950, *Trans. Amer. Inst. Elect. Engrs.* **69**, 961.
287. and VAN DE GRAAF, R. J. 1947, *J. appl. Phys.* **18**, 327.
288. SAFFORD, F. J., and CLOUD, R. W. 1941, *Trans. Amer. Inst. Elect. Engrs.* **60**, 132.
289. VALLE, G. 1950, *Nuovo Cimento*, **7**, 174; 1952, **9**, 145.
290. VARNEY, R. N. 1935, *Phys. Rev.* **47**, 483.
291. WARE, A. A. 1951, *Phil. Trans. Roy. Soc.* A, **243**, 197.
292. WEISSLER, G. L. 1956, *Handbuch d. Phys.* Vol. 21 (Leipzig).
293. and LEE, P. O. 1952, *J. Opt. Soc. Amer.* **42**, 200.
294. LEE, P. O., and MOHR, E. I. 1952, *J. Opt. Soc. Amer.* **42**, 84.
295. WHITE, H. J. 1936, *Phys. Rev.* **49**, 507.
296. WHITEHEAD, S. 1939, *J. Inst. Elect. Engrs.* **84**, 408.
297. WIEDEMANN, E. 1895, *Z. Elektrochem.* 195.
298. WILKES, A., HOPWOOD, W., and PEACOCK, N. J. 1955, *Nature*, **176**, 837.
299. WILLIAMS, G. C., and TOWNSEND, W. G. (Work at Swansea not yet published.)
300. WILSON, R. R. 1936, *Phys. Rev.* **50**, 1082.
301. WORMELL, T. W. 1953, *Quart. J. Roy. Meteorol. Soc.* **79**, 474.
302. YARNOLD, G. D. 1932, *Phil. Mag.* **13**, 1179.
303. ZELENY, J. 1942, *J. appl. Phys.* **13**, 444.
304. ZUBER. K. 1925, *Ann. Phys.* **76**, 231 (Leipzig).

Index